SOME FUNDAMENTALS OF
PETROLEUM GEOLOGY

SOME FUNDAMENTALS

OF

PETROLEUM

GEOLOGY

BY

G. D. HOBSON, Ph.D.

GEOFFREY CUMBERLEGE

OXFORD UNIVERSITY PRESS

LONDON NEW YORK TORONTO

1954

Oxford University Press, Amen House, London E.C. 4

GLASGOW NEW YORK TORONTO MELBOURNE WELLINGTON
BOMBAY CALCUTTA MADRAS KARACHI CAPE TOWN IBADAN

Geoffrey Cumberlege, Publisher to the University

FOREWORD

THE growth of the oil industry is one of the outstanding features of modern civilization. The story behind it is a fascinating study of the gradual development of perfect co-operation between science and engineering. Yet it was some time before this was achieved; indeed it is interesting to note that until the advent of the present century little use was made of geology in oilfield exploration. During this same period, however, the foundations of the science were being well and truly laid and many of the outstanding principles of petroleum geology were enunciated.

The present century ushered in a greatly increased demand for oil. Drilling had to go deeper, and new areas of exploration and development were opened up. The old haphazard methods of searching for oil were gradually abandoned, and in their place science came to play a preponderant part in the guidance of drilling. The petroleum geologist became the spearhead of exploration, first of all with relatively simple tools, but later on with instruments of increasing accuracy and eventually with the aid of geophysics.

During this period of preoccupation with the main problem of increasing oil supplies, it is curious to note that there was a tendency to neglect for the time being the study of basic principles. The concentration of effort was largely on developing new tools of exploration. However, this position has been redressed more recently by the very fact that the great enrichment of the literature due to a wider knowledge of the world's oil pools has automatically led to a revival of interest in the fundamentals of the science. Petroleum geology has become less and less a mere study of structure, and more and more a study of the stratigraphic history of an area, on the principle that the life-history of the oilfields is interwoven with the history of the rocks.

The very complexity of the problems, and the fact that the answers lie not in one science alone, but often in a combined study of several sciences, has been somewhat of a hindrance to progress, and has resulted in an uneven state of knowledge on the various problems. On some subjects, such as the study of the movement of fluids through the sediments, and the principles governing the accumulation of gas and oil, a considerable measure of agreement has been reached, but other problems, such as the actual origin of the oil itself, are still highly debatable. There is therefore room for a new volume which attempts to clear the ground on some of these basic principles, and to focus attention on the more important opinions which have been formulated on different aspects of the problems.

This book has been written primarily for those who are deeply interested in the basic principles of petroleum geology. Its author is one who has studied his subject with infinite patience and with a wide knowledge of the literature. He brings to bear on the problems a detached mind which is equally at home with geology and the basic sciences. Those who read it must not expect to find ready-made solutions to every problem. That is not its purpose, but the aim is rather to stimulate interest and discussion with a view to further progress in the science.

V. C. ILLING

CONTENTS

PREFACE

THE modern oil industry is generally considered to have begun with the drilling of the Drake well in 1859, and from that time the study of petroleum geology necessarily increased. After nearly a century of rapid growth thoughts on fundamental aspects of petroleum geology ought to be showing very definite trends, with considerable cohesion between the various hypotheses in use. In particular it should be possible to sift the more valuable ideas from those which are no longer tenable. Moreover, any attempt to give in historical sequence the various hypotheses which have been or still are current would involve repetition of much that has already been written many times in the voluminous literature on this subject. Accordingly, this little book has been prepared with the basic intention of presenting so far as possible what, in the present state of knowledge, seems to the author to be broadly on the right track. Admittedly it includes excursions into by-ways in places, mainly for purposes of demonstrating particular points, but an attempt has been made to avoid setting up too many Aunt Sallies which have only to be knocked down immediately. It is, however, too much to hope that the general path indicated will prove in the end to be near the truth at all points. The most that can be expected in some cases is that the discussion may have added to the definition of the problem. Nevertheless, if a series of ideas has been presented, together with methods of approach, which will ultimately stir in some reader thoughts which will contribute to the solution of even one of the many outstanding problems of petroleum geology, the task undertaken will have been worth while.

Only a few of the fundamental problems of petroleum geology are discussed in any detail; there are many to which no reference is made and others which have received only brief mention. Perhaps it may be possible to make good some of the omissions on a future occasion. Even where there has been extensive discussion the conclusions are not always so clear-cut as could have been wished. This arises partly from the inadequacy of the observations and experiments.

No attempt has been made to give an exhaustive series of references, but among those listed are some intended to serve as a key to wider reading. Such wider reading, coupled with careful observation and thought, is vital in the case of students.

I am deeply indebted to my colleagues Professor V. C. Illing, Dr. C. J. May and Mr. S. E. Coomber, and to Mr. H. R. Lovely for reading the manuscript, for helpful criticism, and for valuable suggestions. Also I am grateful to Miss R. E. Marks, who has encouraged and even urged me to go into print on this fascinating subject. Misses A. Copas and B. Carter kindly undertook the typing and retyping, while Messrs. A. L. Greig and K. W. Roe, and Miss A. D. Baldry have greatly assisted by converting rough sketches into acceptable diagrams. My wife, Mrs. E. M. Snelling and Mrs. V. Soper have given considerable help with the proofs and Index.

Lastly, I am further indebted to Professor V. C. Illing, who first introduced me to petroleum geology, for writing the Foreword to this book.

G. D. H.

I

THE NATURE OF AN OIL ACCUMULATION

THE word petroleum is used in several senses. By derivation it means rock oil, and is therefore applied to mineral oil as found in the earth's crust. In a wider sense it is sometimes used to cover a variety of dominantly hydrocarbon complexes which range from natural gas through mineral oil to solid waxes and bitumens or asphalts. With the occasional exception of natural gas each of these substances is a mixture of many compounds. The substances are related and, indeed, some of the lower molecular-weight hydrocarbons of mineral oil are commonly present in small amounts in natural gas, while the higher molecular-weight compounds in mineral oil are identical with or very similar to some of the compounds present in natural mineral waxes and asphalts.

Although it is convenient to make the subdivision into gases, liquids, and solids, it must be recognized that there are occasions when the distinction between the last two is not easy, and so very viscous oils may be found grading almost imperceptibly into soft asphalts. However, in the bulk of natural occurrences of petroleum (*s.l.*) the grouping is easily applied when the substances are examined under surface conditions.

From the point of view of occurrence of the above substances it is noteworthy that mineral oil and natural gas are usually found as a general impregnation of the host rock, whereas some of the more notable deposits of mineral wax and some types of asphalt exist in vein form, i.e. filling joints or other fissures in rocks. There are, however, numerous instances where asphalt occurs as a pore-filling in the same way as oil and gas. In addition there are the famous asphalt lakes and other surface asphalt deposits such as those of the Middle East. The commercial exploitation of natural gas and crude oil is on a far larger scale than that of mineral wax or asphalt, and therefore the mode of occurrence of the first two substances will alone be discussed in detail. Oil and gas are found under similar conditions, and hence in the following pages much that is written about oil accumulations could be applied equally well in describing gas accumulations.

Occurrences of mineral oil or natural gas are relatively common, but commercial accumulations of these substances are much less frequent.

The latter are, however, of the main interest, and it is to them that the chief attention will be paid. The terms 'oilfield' and 'oil pool' are in use for oil accumulations which are of commercial interest. It has been suggested that 'oil pool' should be used for a single accumulation. Thus an 'oilfield', i.e. the oil development on one structural or similar feature, would consist of one or more oil pools according as there are one or more reservoir rocks yielding oil.

The areal extent and oil content of oilfields vary widely. The largest fields known include Burgan (Kuwait), covering 135 sq. miles, and East Texas (U.S.A.) 203 sq. miles, while Kirkuk (Iraq) is 60 miles long and has an average width of about 2 miles. Published estimates of the recoverable oil reserves of Burgan and East Texas have been, respectively, 10,000–12,000 million barrels, and 4,000–6,000 million barrels. It should be noted, however, that the volume of recoverable oil is substantially smaller than the volume of oil in place in the reservoir in each case, because it is not possible to extract all the oil from an oil accumulation by means of wells. It is not easy to ascertain what is the smallest oil accumulation which has been exploited, but there are numerous cases where a single well has yielded a few hundred or a few thousand barrels of oil. (1 barrel = 42 U.S. gal. = 5·6 cu. ft.)

Reservoir rock. The rock in which the oil occurs is known as the reservoir rock. The oil may occupy any of a variety of openings which are found in rocks. These openings include the pores between the constituent grains of the rock, cavities in fossils, solution cavities, open joints, fissures, and partings along bedding planes. Pores are the commonest type of openings, and in most reservoir rocks they provide the bulk of the oil- and gas-storage space. The openings confer on the rock the property of porosity* but the presence of porosity alone is not sufficient to make a rock a satisfactory reservoir rock. In a good reservoir rock the pores must be relatively large and continuously connected by openings (throats) of adequate size. Continuous connexion of the pores and other openings gives permeability or fluid-transmitting capacity, and thereby permits oil or gas to flow through the reservoir rock. Flow at a reasonable rate is essential for the normal method of recovery of oil or gas by means of wells.

It is not easy to define the most typical values for porosity and permeability in reservoir rocks, but the following figures may serve as a general guide: Bulnes and Fitting[2]† plotted data for 2,200 measurements on sandstones and for 1,200 measurements on dolomitic limestones.

---

* See Appendix II for definitions.
† Superior numerals refer to references listed at the end of each chapter.

These plots showed that the bulk of the sandstones had porosities in the range 10–30 per cent., whereas for the limestones the range was 5–25 per cent. The sandstone permeability values lay mainly in the range 10–1,200 millidarcys and for limestones most of the values were under 100 mD and probably half of them were under 10 mD.

A series of conventional test plugs (1 in. long and ¾ in. diameter), cut at random from a core of uniform Gulf Coast sandstone and from a

TABLE I

(After Bulnes and Fitting[2])

Sandstone			Limestone		
Permeability			Permeability		
Parallel to bedding	Normal to bedding	Porosity	Parallel to bedding	Normal to bedding	Porosity
mD	mD	%	mD	mD	%
2,650		26·1	150		27·5
6,300		29·6	1850		6·5
2,400		25·8	1,520,000		26·0*
620		26·1	2,670,000		36·5*
	450	23·4		0·1	7·0
	1100	25·7		0·1	7·0

* A cavernous opening is included in the bulk volume.

piece of cavernous limestone of about the same size, gave the data of Table I.

Atkinson and Johnston[1] studied long cores from fractured Ellenburger dolomitic limestone reservoir rocks. Their measurements showed the average total connected porosity to be 3·3 per cent., while the matrix porosity averaged 1·51 per cent., making the average for the connected fractures and vugs 1·79 per cent. The highest bulk porosity was 7·2 per cent., and the highest fracture and vug porosity 5·6 per cent. These figures indicate some of the possibilities for certain types and conditions of limestones, although Atkinson and Johnston note that: 'It should be realised, however, that there are important changes in lithology within the Ellenburger reservoir from which these cores were taken and that it is extremely unlikely that the section analyzed is typical of the entire reservoir.'

In most oilfields the reservoir rocks are sedimentary rocks, but oil accumulations are known also in igneous and metamorphic rocks. However, when oil or natural gas occurs in the latter types of rocks it is always near to sedimentary rocks; it never occurs in the middle of an igneous or metamorphic rock province.

The commonest reservoir rocks are sands, sandstones, grits, conglomerates, and limestones of various types. The arenaceous rocks and many of the limestones are among the coarser-textured sediments, and therefore, in the absence of extensive cementation or recrystallization, they have larger pores and higher permeabilities than clays or shales. Nevertheless, there are a few instances of shales serving as reservoir rocks, e.g. Florence, Colorado. The shales which act as reservoir rocks are extensively jointed or fissured. The fluid-transmitting capacity of even a fine crack is high, and hence joints and fissures give to a rock-mass a permeability in bulk in certain directions which is far above that of the rock without fractures. At the same time the volume of the fractures may be small, and by no means a large fraction of the storage space available in the form of pores. The fractures and fissures may make a satisfactory reservoir rock from a rock which, in their absence, would be most unpromising.

Metamorphic rocks and many igneous rocks are compact and have only small pore spaces. However, such features as joints and openings developed by weathering or structural disturbance increase their permeability and storage capacity, and as a consequence enable them occasionally to function as reservoir rocks. Oil accumulations in igneous rocks occur at Furbero, Mexico, and at Lytton Springs, Texas; an accumulation in metamorphic rock is exploited at Edison, California.

A reservoir rock may be only a few feet thick or it may be several hundred feet thick. An oilfield may have one or a number of reservoir rocks. The individual reservoirs may be separated by a few feet or by hundreds of feet of non-productive strata. When the reservoirs are of reasonable thickness and separated by suitable amounts of barren rock, they can be treated independently in oil production. When they are very close together and thin, oil may be produced from a group of reservoirs simultaneously. In California there are oilfields with a thousand or more feet of closely interbedded oil-bearing and non-oil-bearing rocks, and a single well may draw oil production from a considerable thickness of such a sequence.

Oil has been produced from reservoir rocks at depths ranging virtually from the grass roots down to well over 10,000 ft. Currently, the deepest oil production is from 17,500–17,892 ft. at North Coles Levee, Kern County, California, and there is no reason to believe that oil will not be obtained from greater depths. The deepest well yet drilled in search of oil has reached 21,482 ft., and is at Paloma, Kern County, California.

Fluid distribution. In a reservoir rock of uniform texture the arrangement of the fluids is determined by their densities, i.e. gas—if present and free—overlies oil which in turn overlies water. Oil densities under reservoir conditions vary considerably, but are almost always less than 1·0 gm./c.c.; the water, which normally is saline, has a density slightly exceeding 1·0 gm./c.c. (for details see Chapter II). The oil has gas in solution, the amount of the dissolved gas being determined by the composition of the oil, the composition of the gas, the relative amounts of these two substances, and the temperature and pressure. If the physical conditions and the composition of the oil and gas are fixed, then an increase in the proportion of gas will eventually lead to a condition under which the oil is saturated with gas. For lower proportions of gas under the same temperature and pressure the gas-oil solution will be described as under-saturated; for higher proportions of gas the gas-oil solution will be saturated and the excess gas will occur in the free state in a zone, known as the gas cap, overlying the gas-oil solution. When there is no free gas the gas-oil solution will occupy the highest available part of the reservoir rock which is suitably sealed so as to retain the oil in place.

The interrelations between the physical conditions and the states of the hydrocarbon accumulation are well displayed by the conventional phase diagrams. It has been found that for many purposes a hydrocarbon accumulation can be represented approximately as a two-component system, crude oil being one component and natural gas the other. For fixed proportions and compositions of these two components (e.g. system X) oilfields with gas caps must have physical conditions exemplified by points within the two-phase region (Fig. 1). Should the physical conditions be depicted by points above the bubble-point curve there will be no free gas, i.e. only one phase (a liquid), and the crude oil will be under-saturated with gas. When the temperature and pressure are represented by points below or to the right of the dew-point curve, again there will be only one phase, in this case the gaseous phase. If we consider examples of the liquid phase and the gaseous phase under physical conditions which progressively approach the critical point, these phases will become more and more similar in properties (density, viscosity, &c.) until identicality is reached at the critical point.

In some reservoirs the pressure and temperature are not far above the critical point of the hydrocarbon system, and there is only a single gaseous phase. On reduction of the pressure some liquid separates, and such an accumulation is described as a distillate or a condensate reservoir, of which a considerable number are now known. It is the behaviour on pressure and/or temperature change with passage from the one-phase to the two-phase region which affords information permitting the state in the one-phase region to be identified conventionally as liquid or gas.

It appears that in a number of so-called condensate reservoirs the conditions may be most closely represented by a point just within the two-phase region and slightly above the critical temperature, because

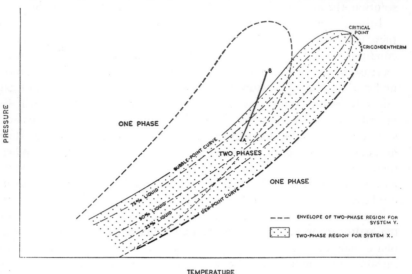

Fig. 1. In the case of system Y the ratio of the gas and liquid components is greater than for system X. Apart from the marking of the envelope of the two-phase region for system Y, all the markings and labelling on the diagram refer to system X.

dark oil-rings have been reported down dip. In this case also pressure reduction would lead at first to condensation of liquid, and then to revaporization at still lower pressures.

The demarcation between the gas, oil, and water zones is not sharp; in each case there is a transition zone in which there is a downward change from mainly gas to mainly oil, or from mainly oil to water. The thickness of the transition zones is dependent on the physical properties of the fluids, and on the pore forms, sizes and size distribution in the reservoir rocks. Other things being equal, the coarser the rock the thinner the transition zone. The transition zone can be several feet and more in thickness.

Even above the transition zones the so-called oil and gas zones are probably never completely filled with gas-oil solution or with gas, respectively. Observations have shown that the pores within the oil zone commonly have an average water content of 10 per cent. or more. The average water content of the oil zone can exceed 40 per cent. in some reservoirs without this water flowing to a well in important amounts in the normal course of oil production. Similarly, the gas cap may contain measurable amounts of water and/or oil. The water in the oil or gas zones is referred to as connate or interstitial water, the latter term probably being preferable.

Most oil reservoirs appear to have fairly considerable quantities of interstitial water in the oil zones, but there are exceptional cases, such as the Oklahoma City oilfield, Oklahoma, in which the oil has some unusual action upon the reservoir rock, and this appears to have precluded the presence of interstitial water in normal amounts.

The interstitial water can be considered to occur in three forms (Fig. 2): (a) as a thin wetting film covering the surfaces of the mineral grains; (b) as collars around the points of contact of the mineral grains; and (c) as complete fillings of rock pores which have unusually small throats connecting them with adjacent pores. The volume of water attributable to the wetting films is small because the films are only a few molecules thick. In many reservoir rocks the collars around the grain contacts contain the bulk of the interstitial water. For spherical grains of uniform size comparable with sand grains, and systematically packed, it is possible to calculate the amount of water which should be present in collars. The value obtained is in general agreement with the interstitial water contents reported for various oil reservoirs. When, due to irregularities of grain size, form, or packing, the pores within the reservoir rock vary markedly in size, and in particular have considerable variations in connecting throat size, pores bounded by smaller than average throats will be full of water. The geometrical considerations are too complex to permit prediction of a throat-size–pore-size relationship, but on general grounds it can be expected that some rocks may have considerable numbers of pores completely filled with water even though these pores are within the general oil zone. Extension of this concept leads to the prediction of the occurrence of water-saturated streaks and layers within an oil zone, and such conditions are known to occur in some reservoir rocks. A cap-rock is an extreme case of the phenomenon of fine-pored rocks in association with hydrocarbon accumulations being water-saturated.

Factors responsible for retaining an oil accumulation. The cross-sectional form of the reservoir rock is widely variable in different oilfields, but an anticlinal form is generally considered to be most typical. Consequently an anticline will be used for purposes of illustration

(Fig. 3). If the oil pool has a gas cap, the gas will occupy the crestal part of the anticline; oil will occur beneath the gas, and water still farther down. The oil and gas are prevented from escaping upwards by the

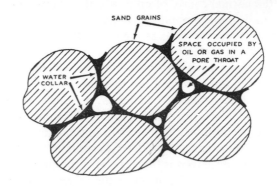

SECTION THROUGH GRAIN CONTACTS

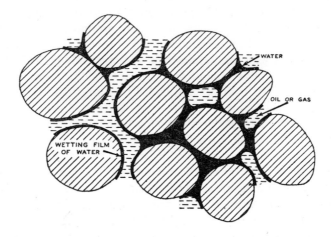

SECTION ROUGHLY PARALLEL TO AXES OF SOME PORE THROATS

FIG. 2. The thickness of the wetting film of water is grossly enlarged.

cap-rock. This sealing formation is fine-grained and/or compact, free from fractures, and has a negligible or no 'permeability' to oil and gas. The displacement pressure of this formation is large (see Chapter IV and Appendix II). It is obvious that it must have those properties, otherwise gas and oil would have moved upwards into it and it would have become a part of the reservoir rock complex if, indeed, the hydrocarbons had not escaped completely. Typical cap-rocks are clays and shales, but compact or silicified limestones can also act as cap-rocks. Clays and shales are probably more efficacious than the others because of their fineness of grain size, plasticity, and their ability to undergo considerable deformation without fracturing.

No name has been given to the rock underlying the oil- or gas-bearing part of the reservoir rock, but it is clear that this rock must have properties similar to those of the cap-rock. If this were not the case, in all fields where the oil or gas zone is not continuously underlain by

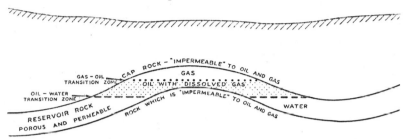

FIG. 3. Section through a typical anticlinal oil and gas accumulation, showing the various components and the distribution of the fluids.

water-saturated reservoir rock the underlying rock would become a hydrocarbon-bearing extension of the 'reservoir' rock.

Oil reservoirs have many forms, but the number of different sealing elements involved is quite small. Thus in an anticlinal oil accumulation the hydrocarbons are held in place by arched cap-rock, water in the extension of the reservoir rock, and often by an underlying sealing rock. In a fault accumulation, part of the lateral confinement is provided by sealing rock being placed opposite the reservoir rock as a result of the fault displacement or by impermeable rock (fault gouge) generated in that position by the faulting. Monoclinal oil accumulations may be sealed up-dip in a number of ways. Often the reservoir rock wedges out up-dip, in which case the under- and over-lying sealing rocks come together and keep the oil and gas in place. In some cases the reservoir rock is continuous to the ground surface, and sealing results from the blocking effect of bitumen or wax in the reservoir rock pores near the outcrop. This bitumen or wax arises as a result of inspissation of oil in the reservoir rock due to evaporation or to various chemical reactions near the earth's surface. Extensive cementation up-dip from the oil accumulation sometimes gives the seal in that direction, while a diminution in grain size and pore size up-dip, with a consequent change in penetrability by oil and gas, and in water-holding (and oil- and gas-excluding) properties, frequently contributes to the retention of an oil accumulation.

The set of factors which operate so as to hold the oil or gas accumulation in position constitutes a trap. It is a common practice to give the trap a name which is descriptive of the form, e.g. fault trap, anticlinal trap, but it is clear that the fault displacement, or the reversal of dip in the case of an anticline, provides only one of the elements necessary to hold the fluid hydrocarbon accumulation in place. It is, however, the element which is peculiar to that form of trap.

There have been numerous elaborate discussions of proposed classifications for oil and gas traps, but basically there are relatively few fundamental features, although these features may arise in a variety of ways: (a) arched form of the top of the reservoir rock (this may be depositional, erosional, structural, or due to compaction); and (b) up-dip termination of the reservoir rock (this may be due to depositional factors, to erosion, to faulting, or to intrusion, or to the absence of action up-dip of an agent responsible for the development of secondary porosity and permeability in reservoirs where the favourable physical properties are not original, or to the action up-dip of an agent which obliterates the original favourable properties of a reservoir rock).

The post-lithefaction changes which increase the porosity and permeability of rocks include leaching of limestones at unconformities, dolomitization, partial replacement which is reputed to have developed openings in some shaly rocks, and jointing commonly caused by structural disturbance. On rare occasions the joints and other openings may result from thermal changes connected with igneous intrusions.

Some traps are simple, i.e. they have one of the special features indicated above, but many are complex, involving more than one of these features. Thus trapping may be due to anticlinal form in one part of an oil accumulation and to faulting in another part, or to a combination of faulting or folding with one or more of the other forms of up-dip termination of porosity and permeability.

REFERENCES

1. ATKINSON, B., and JOHNSTON, D., *Petrol Tech.*, **11**, A.I.M.M.E. Tech. Pub. No. 2432 (1948).
2. BULNES, A. C., and FITTING, R. U., ibid., **8**, A.I.M.M.E. Tech. Pub. No. 1791 (1945).

II

THE RESERVOIR FLUIDS:
THEIR COMPOSITION AND PROPERTIES

Natural gas

THE principal component of most natural gases, i.e. those associated with petroliferous areas, is methane, and this compound usually forms 60–95 per cent. by volume of the gas. Ethane, propane, butanes, pentanes, hexanes, and some higher paraffins are present in smaller amounts, the isomers usually being less abundant than the normal (straight-chain) compounds. Naphthenes and aromatics, when present, generally occur in very small amounts, because they have lower vapour pressures than the lightest paraffins.[6]

Carbon dioxide is sometimes present, and natural gases consisting almost wholly of this compound are known. Hydrogen sulphide contents up to about 13 per cent. have been reported. This seems to be the commonest sulphur compound in natural gases. However, most of the sulphur in the gas from the Granite Wash zone of the Texas Panhandle is stated to be in the form of ethyl, propyl, and butyl mercaptans rather than as hydrogen sulphide.[1] Sachanen[17] observes that the methyl and ethyl mercaptans may be as high as 0·5–1·0 per cent. in some sulphurous gases.

Figures given by Huntingdon[6] indicate that the approximate average nitrogen content of the U.S.A. natural gas reserves is about 7·9 per cent., the values ranging from 2·4 per cent. in the Gulf Coast area to 16·3 per cent. at Hugoton. Wells in the Westbrook field, Mitchell County, Texas, are reported to have produced gas with 84–96 per cent. of nitrogen.[2]

Huntingdon[6] states that almost without exception helium is found in natural gases in U.S.A., but the concentration is usually low. On rare occasions it constitutes 8–9 per cent. by volume, but is mostly less than 0·25 per cent. and often only a few hundredths or thousandths of 1 per cent. For commercial extraction 1 per cent. of helium seems to be about the minimum concentration.

Frost, who is quoted by Huntingdon, contends that hydrogen is present in natural gas, and on the basis of certain assumptions he estimates the concentration to be 0·004–0·05 per cent. by volume. Shallow gas flows at the base of the glacial drift in Michigan have given up to 26 per cent. of hydrogen. Newcombe[12] notes that these shallow gas flows occur at the base of the drift, especially in areas where important oil- and gas-bearing formations occur immediately beneath the drift. In the case of the analysis of drift gas quoted in Table II, the ratio of nitrogen to oxygen is such as to make it possible for the latter to have

TABLE II

Component	Masjid-i-Sulaiman[20]	Topila[9]	Alma[7]	Augusta[7]	Kilgore[7]	Gray[1] County	Washentaw County	Roma[22]
	% by vol.	% by vol.	% by vol.	% by vol.	% by vol.	% by vol.	% by vol.	% by vol.
CH4 .	45·3	2·02	99·2	10·6	36·7	89·02	69·0	74·6
C2H6 .	13·5	0·05	..	1·6	14·5	4·02	..	
C3H8 .	15·3	0·13	..	..	23·5	4·20	..	16·3*
C4H10 .	10·8	0·21	..	..	14·9	2·90	..	
Higher hydrocarbons .	4·7	1·59	..	..	10·4	1·86	..	
H2S .	10·4	trace	..	..	..	..	..	..
CO2 .	..	95·75	0·2	0·1	..	..	0·6	1·5
N2 .	..	..	0·6	85·6	..	..	3·6	3·4†
He .	trace	..	..	2·13	..	..	..	..
H2 .	..	..	..	..	..	..	26·0	..
O2 .	..	..	..	..	..	..	0·8	..
CO .	..	..	..	..	..	..	..	5·8
						Composite casing-head gas	Drift gas	

* The item of 16·3 per cent. is reported as: ethane and higher paraffins 9·8 per cent., benzene series 5·0 per cent., olefines 1·5 per cent.
† Nitrogen and other residual gases.

been derived from air together with much of the former. Frost expresses views which cast doubt on some of the cases where oxygen has been reported in natural gas.

Crude oil and natural gasoline

Composition. Crude oil is composed mainly of carbon and hydrogen. Sulphur, oxygen, and nitrogen, when present, occur in much smaller amounts. Redwood[14] gave the range of carbon contents of petroleum as 79·5–88·7 per cent. and of hydrogen 9·7–13·6 per cent.

Sachanen[17] states that for a series of crudes the sulphur content ranged from 0·04 per cent. (Pennsylvania) to 5·2 per cent. (Panuco), while the nitrogen content ranged from 0·012 per cent. (Embleton, Pennsylvania) to 0·802 per cent. (Ojai, California). He also notes that crudes rich in sulphur are usually rich in nitrogen.

The problem of ascertaining what compounds exist in crude petroleum is exceedingly difficult. Undoubtedly many of the compounds cannot be distilled at atmospheric pressure without decomposition, and hence separation by distillation under such conditions is impossible. Distillation under reduced pressure may still involve thermal decomposition of some compounds. Furthermore, the complexity of the mixture and the closeness of the boiling-points of succeeding members of a given hydrocarbon series, as well as the similarity of boiling-points

TABLE III

(After Nelson[11])

Source of crude	Composition				
	C	H	N	O	S
	%	%	%	%	%
Pennsylvania . .	85·5	14·2			
Mecock, West Virginia .	83·6	12·9	..	3·6	..
Humboldt, Kansas .	85·6	12·4	..	..	0·37
Healdton, Oklahoma .	85·0	12·9	..	..	0·76
Coalinga, California .	86·4	11·7	1·14	..	0·60
Beaumont, Texas .	85·7	11·0	2·61		0·70
Mexico . . .	83·0	11·0	1·7		4·30
Baku . . .	86·5	12·0	..	1·5	..
Colombia . . .	85·6	11·9	0·54	..	..

for members of different hydrocarbon series, limit the degree of separation which can be achieved by fractional distillation, even for members which are stable at their boiling-points. Compounds identified in some distillates may not be present in the original crudes, having been formed by molecular changes during the course of distillation.

Since there are considerable differences in the amounts and nature of the different types of compounds recognized in distillates from different crudes, it is reasonable to infer that the crudes themselves differ considerably in the amounts and types of compounds which they contain.

Differences in colour, density, viscosity, and other properties of crude oils are also indicative of differences in composition.

Natural gasoline is a volatile hydrocarbon liquid extracted from 'wet' natural gas, i.e. gas containing some of the higher boiling-point hydrocarbons, including the light components of gasoline. Natural gasolines have been found to contain 80 per cent. or more of paraffins. Both *n*- and *iso*-paraffins occur, in proportions varying according to the source. Naphthenes may sometimes amount to 10–20 per cent., while aromatics do not exceed 1–2 per cent.[16] Non-hydrocarbon compounds, mostly mercaptans, are usually insignificant in amount in natural gasolines.

It is reasonable to expect that some, at least, of the higher molecular-weight compounds in crude oils will belong to the same series or types as those which have been recognized in natural gasolines. The proportions may, however, be different. This proves to be the case, for the main types of hydrocarbons recognized in crude oils are the paraffins, naphthenes, and aromatics. In addition there are hybrids which have more than one kind of structure in a single molecule. Both the naphthene and aromatic hydrocarbons may be monocyclic and polycyclic, and the naphthenes occur as saturated five- and six-membered rings. The paraffins may be straight-chain or branched. The proportions of the main types of hydrocarbons differ in different crude oils, and crude oils have been broadly classified on the basis of these proportions.

Sachanen[17] (p. 316)* considers that the evidence warrants the belief that naphthenic acids exist in crude oils, but that the origin of low molecular-weight fatty acids is doubtful. These fatty acids can be formed by the decomposition of certain unstable high molecular-weight acids during distillation.

The nitrogen bases detected in distillates appear to arise from the decomposition of some complex neutral nitrogen compounds. It has not, however, been proved that all the low molecular-weight sulphur compounds reported, such as mercaptans and sulphides, are decomposition products. Crudes contain resinous and asphaltic substances in which oxygen and sulphur are present[17] (p. 350).

Triebs found complex organic compounds known as porphyrins to occur in some crude oils. The oils he examined were principally of Tertiary age and mainly from Europe. A few came from U.S.A., and one sample from Trinidad; the former were of Palaeozoic age. The porphyrins were desoxophyllerythrin and mesoporphyrin and their degradation products. The former can be derived from chlorophyll and the latter from haemin, which is a component of haemoglobin. The chlorophyll-derived compounds seemed to be predominant in many cases, and Triebs showed that in many oils the porphyrins were present as vanadium salts. In most of the crudes the etioporphyrins alone were found, and these are the decarboxylated derivatives of desoxophyllerythrin and mesoporphyrin.[18]

Mineral ash. Most crude oils yield a small amount of ash, and dense oils generally give more than light oils. Southwick has stated that it is

---

* A page number in parentheses following a superior numeral showing the reference number of the publication indicates the relevant page in the publication.

difficult to obtain reproducible quantities in laboratory studies, while Thomas[21] notes that the time of settling affects the figures. The latter statement indicates that some of the so-called ash must come from relatively coarse suspended particles. Nevertheless, Thomas notes that filtration of crudes which have stood for a long time rarely removes more than half of the inorganic matter, and that part removed usually consists of SiO_2, Fe_2O_3, CaO, &c., material which could be obtained from wind-borne dust, tank or pipe scale, and similar sources.

Some Persian crudes[21] yielded 0·003–0·006 per cent. of ash. A series of analyses of this ash gave the following data:

	%		%
SiO_2	12·1–52·8	Fe_2O_3, Al_2O_3, TiO_2	13·1–37·1
CaO	6·1–12·7	NiO	1·4–10·7
MgO	0·2–9·1	SO_3	1–7
V_2O_5	14·0–38·5		

Traces of Ba, Sr, Sn, Mo, Cu, and Mn were detected.

Analyses of ashes from some U.S.A. crudes have yielded the following figures:

	%		%
K_2O	0·0–0·9	P_2O_5	0·0–0·1
Li_2O	0·0–0·2	Cl	0·1–4·6

Other elements recorded as traces in ashes include Au, Ag, Pb, Co, As, Cr. In addition to these Pachachi[13] has reported Zn, B, Sb, Ga, Tl, and Rh in the ashes from crudes. For comparison it may be noted that Sverdrup, Johnson, and Fleming[19] (pp. 176–7) list the following elements in solution in gas-free sea-water: Cl, Na, Mg, S, Ca, K, Br, C, Sr, B, Si, F, N, Al, Ru, Li, P, Ba, I, As, Fe, Mn, Cu, Zn, Pb, Se, Cs, U, Mo, Th, Ce, Ag, V, La, T, Ni, Sc, Hg, Au, Ra, Cd, Co, Sn, the bulk of them in very minute quantities. Some or all of these elements might be taken up by marine organisms, with the possibility of their ultimate incorporation, otherwise than in the interstitial water, in the sediments from which oil is formed.

Perhaps the most surprising feature of the ashes from petroleum is the high proportion of V_2O_5 in some cases. Ashes from some asphalts have shown as much as 43 per cent. of this oxide.

The ash may be derived from colloidal metallic oxides or sulphides, or from metallo-organic compounds. Filtration of one Mexican crude through an absorbent removed all the sulphur and vanadium, and hence it has been inferred that in this crude the vanadium was present as a colloidal sulphide.

The free sulphur reported in crudes probably arises from the oxidation of hydrogen sulphide dissolved in the crude. Thus the crude from Beaumont, Texas, contains much hydrogen sulphide and after aeration deposits sulphur.[15]

Specific gravity. Examination of data for over 400 crudes, mainly from U.S.A. but some from the Middle East, Mexico, and Venezuela, showed that specific gravities under surface conditions ranged from 0·7275 to 1·0217. Eighty per cent. of the values lay between 0·8299 and 0·9402, and 90 per cent. between 0·7972 and 0·9529. It was noteworthy that the distributions of specific gravity values differed considerably in different regions.

Viscosity. A study of viscosity data, obtained at 100° F. for nearly 200 crudes, again mainly from U.S.A., showed a range from 0·007 stoke to 13 stokes. However, 80 per cent. of the values were in the range 0·035–0·117 stoke and 90 per cent. in the range 0·023–0·231 stoke. (The stoke is poise/density.)

From some points of view the precise values of the specific gravity and viscosity data for crude oils under surface conditions are not important. The extreme values in each case are in a sense freaks, but do indicate the gradation into asphalts at one end and into condensates at the other. It is fairly certain in some cases that the heavy oil is the residue of a crude which formerly had a greater proportion of lighter and more volatile components, or that its heaviness is in part due to reaction with substances which have gained access to the reservoir rock. The freak light oils are probably the lighter components of a crude the heavier fractions of which are to be found elsewhere. Furthermore, the specific gravity and viscosity values quoted will differ from those which will obtain under reservoir conditions at a considerable depth in the earth's crust. In a reservoir the generally higher temperature and the presence of dissolved gas in the oil will cause both the specific gravities and the viscosities to be lower than for surface conditions. As an example of the large differences in viscosity between surface and reservoir conditions which can occur, the following data for a crude from North Lindsay, Oklahoma, are given: 0·16 centipoise at 4,576 p.s.i.; 1·12 centipoises at 0 p.s.i. Even larger differences have been observed.

Surface tension. The surface tension of crude oils under surface conditions is about 30 dynes/cm. The values for a small number of crudes listed by Muskat ranged 27·5–34·1 dynes/cm.

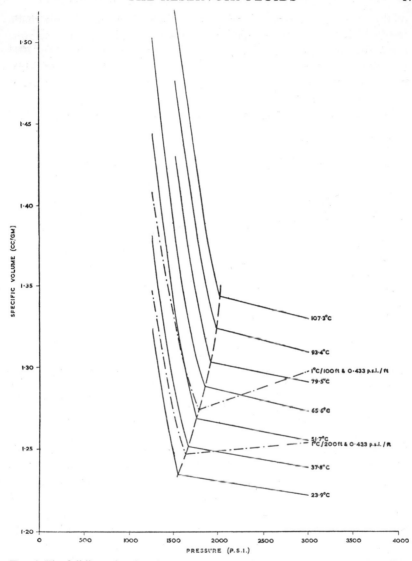

FIG. 4. The full lines give data for Dominguez crude with 5·6 per cent. (by weight) of gas; the broken lines show the predicted behaviour on burial at increasing depths, assuming a surface temperature of 15° C., a pressure gradient of 0·433 p.s.i./ft., and temperature gradients of 1° C./100 ft. and 1° C./200 ft.

Dissolved natural gas, and also carbon dioxide, has a very marked effect on the surface tension of crude oil, and at pressures of 800–1,600 p.s.i. the values may be from one-half to one-quarter or even less of the values at atmospheric pressure. When allowance is also made for the higher temperature which may obtain at depth in an oil reservoir, the reduction in surface tension is even greater, and Muskat[10] (p. 101) has estimated that for pressures and temperatures in excess of 3,000 p.s.i. and 150° F., respectively, the surface tension of crudes may be of the order of 1 dyne/cm.

Interfacial tension. Thirty-four crudes examined by Livingston[8] had

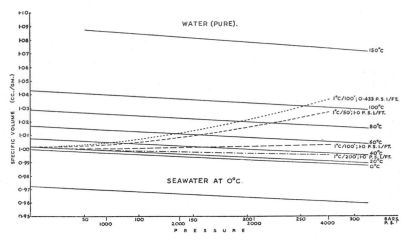

FIG. 5. The data for pure water are from *The Handbook of Physical Constants,* Geol. Soc. of America, Special Paper No. 56, and those for sea-water from H. V. Sverdrup, M. W. Johnson, and R. H. Fleming, *The Oceans,* p. 1053. The broken lines show the predicted behaviour of pure water on increased burial, assuming a surface temperature of 15° C., and different pressure gradients and temperature gradients.

interfacial tensions against brines ranging 13·6–34·3 dynes/cm. at 70° F. The average value was 20·4 dynes/cm. Bartell and Merrill obtained values of 13–25 dynes/cm. for thirteen oils at temperatures which are not given.

An increase in the dissolved gas content of a crude increases the interfacial tension of the oil against water. The actual form of the change varies with the crude, but increases of 3 dynes/cm. occur for pressure rises to about 1,000 p.s.i. For pressure increases with a fixed composition (constant amount of dissolved gas) there is a decrease in interfacial tension.

Compressibility and thermal expansion. Both salt water and crude oil, with or without gas in solution, are slightly compressible, and they also expand on heating. Fig. 4 shows the relationship between specific volume and pressure for one gas-oil system at a series of temperatures. Fig. 5 gives similar data for pure water at a series of temperatures and for seawater at one temperature. Although in both cases the compressibilities are small they are of practical importance in oil production in certain fields.

Oilfield waters

Composition. The concentration and composition of the waters found in oilfields vary widely.

TABLE IV

(The quantities are expressed as parts per million)

Source of water	Total solids	Na*	Ca	Mg	SO₄	Cl	CO₃	HCO₃
Rangely, Colorado, Weber . .	108,053	37,725	3,509	568	973	65,000	0	565
Lander, Wyoming, Tensleep . .	249	34	41	17	13	31	0	230
Kawkawlin, Mich. Dundee . .	258,105	66,280	25,740	4,670	155	161,200	..	60
Bay City, Mich. Salina . .	642,798	21,383	206,300	7,300	0	403,207	..	1,208
East Texas, Texas, Woodbine . .	67,649	24,540	1,388	282	278	40,958	..	569

* Includes any potassium present.

The elements and radicles listed in Table IV do not cover all those that occur in oilfield waters. Thus Li, Ba, and Sr can be present in small amounts, and the same is true of Br, I, and borate, although Br and I sometimes are found in amounts which are unexpectedly relatively large.

Muskat has commented on the fact that the concentration of the solutes in the interstitial water may not be the same as in the associated edge-water.

It appears that some oilfield brines contain small amounts of organic compounds. Organic acids have been identified, and the presence of organic compounds is suggested in some cases by the surface tension differing considerably from the value for pure water.

Viscosity. The viscosity of pure water at atmospheric pressure is as follows:

TABLE V

Temperature	Viscosity	Temperature	Viscosity
°C	cp.	°C	cp.
20	1·009	70	0·407
30	0·800	80	0·357
40	0·654	90	0·317
50	0·549	100	0·284
60	0·470		

At a temperature of 30° C. Bridgman's data indicate that a rise in pressure of 2,000 kg./sq. cm. increased the viscosity of water by about 15 per cent. of the value at atmospheric pressure. The rate of increase was not uniform over this range but was greater in the higher pressure ranges. At higher temperatures there is a comparable relative increase in viscosity as the pressure is increased. The combined effects of increased temperature and pressure as the depth of burial increases may be expected to cause a decrease in the viscosity of water since the former factor is likely to be dominant. Hubbert's calculations[5] give a viscosity of 0·284 centipoise for water at a depth of 3,000 metres.

The viscosity of oilfield water is probably similar to that of pure water under comparable conditions of temperature and pressure. Increase in temperature leads to a marked drop in viscosity, whereas increase in pressure has little effect.

Specific gravity. The specific gravities of oilfield waters at 60° F./60° F. show appreciable variations. Muskat[10] (p. 104) lists a small number of values, and these range 1·0071 to 1·1362. The extent to which these values would be altered under reservoir conditions will depend on the subsurface temperature and pressure, and on whether there is gas dissolved in the water.

Surface tension. Under surface conditions the surface tension of a number of oilfield brines has been found to be in the range 49·5–74·1 dynes/cm. Hocott[4] has shown that the surface tension of oilfield water against gas diminishes as the saturation pressure is increased and also as the temperature rises. In one case the surface tension was almost halved when the saturation pressure was raised to 3,500 p.s.i.

REFERENCES

1. COTNER, V., and CRUM, H. E., *Geology of Natural Gas*, 409, Amer. Assoc. Petrol. Geol., 1935.
2. DOBBIN, C. E., *Geology of Natural Gas*, 1055, Amer. Assoc. Petrol. Geol., 1935.
3. GORANSON, R. W., *Handbook of Physical Constants*, Geol. Soc. of America, Special Paper No. 56.
4. HOCOTT, C. R., *Petroleum Technology*, 1 (4), A.I.M.M.E. Tech. Pub. No. 1006 (1938).
5. HUBBERT, M. K., *J. Geol.*, **48**, 785 (1940).
6. HUNTINGDON, R. K., *Natural Gas and Natural Gasoline*, McGraw-Hill Book Co. Inc., 1950.
7. LEY, H. A., *Geology of Natural Gas*, 1075, Amer. Assoc. Petrol. Geol., 1935.
8. LIVINGSTON, H. K., *Petroleum Technology*, **1**, A.I.M.M.E. Tech. Pub. No. 1001 (1938).
9. MCCONNELL SANDERS, J., *Science of Petroleum*, ii, 868, Oxford University Press, 1938.

10. MUSKAT, M., *Physical Principles of Oil Production*, 101, 104, McGraw-Hill Book Co. Inc., 1949.
11. NELSON, W. L., *Petroleum Refinery Engineering*, 29, McGraw-Hill Book Co. Inc., 3rd edn. 1949.
12. NEWCOMBE, R. B., *Geology of Natural Gas*, 808, 809, Amer. Assoc. Petrol. Geol., 1935.
13. PACHACHI, N., *The Geochemical Aspects of the Origin of Oils of the Oilfields Belt of Iraq*, Ph.D. Thesis, University of London.
14. REDWOOD, B., *Petroleum*, 237, C. Griffin & Co. Ltd., 3rd edn., 1913.
15. REID, E., *Science of Petroleum*, ii, 1033, Oxford University Press, 1938.
16. SACHANEN, A. N., *Science of Petroleum*, v, 56, Oxford University Press, 1950.
17. —— *The Chemical Constituents of Petroleum*, 316, 350, 370, Reinhold Publishing Corporation, 1945.
18. SHEPPARD, C. W., *Fundamental Research on Occurrence and Recovery of Petroleum*, A.P.I., 1943.
19. SVERDRUP, H. V., JOHNSON, M. W., and FLEMING, R. H., *The Oceans*, 176–7, 1053, Prentice-Hall Inc., 1942.
30. THOLE, F. B., *Science of Petroleum*, ii, 894, Oxford University Press, 1938.
31. THOMAS, W. H., *Science of Petroleum*, ii, 1053, Oxford University Press, 1938.
32. WADE, A., *J. Inst. Pet.*, **37**, 703 (1951).

III

ORIGIN OF PETROLEUM

THE problem of the origin of petroleum is as fascinating as it is complex. As a consequence it has been the subject of much speculation. Many hypotheses have been put forward, and these have been summarized or reviewed on a number of occasions.[10, 22] Circumstantial evidence permits some of these hypotheses to be rejected as not being the means by which the oil in oilfields was formed. Others, which as a rule have much in common, but which differ in some vital feature, must be considered as possibilities until the mode of origin of petroleum is more completely determined. The full solution of this problem will call for contributions from geologists, biologists, chemists, biochemists, and physicists. However, in spite of the difficulty and complexity of the problem it is possible to define some of the conditions which must be satisfied by any acceptable hypothesis on oil origin, thereby restricting the field for speculation.

One of the basic general problems of geology which must be continually borne in mind, and wherever possible investigated, relates to how far conditions and processes have been on an average similar in all respects at different dates in the past, and also similar to those now going on. This problem impinges on petroleum geology in more ways than one, and it is certainly of interest in discussions concerning the origin of oil. All too often there is the implicit assumption of substantial uniformity, with little or no consideration given to the consequences which would arise if this assumption is not correct. On general grounds it seems reasonable to expect that the principle is more likely to be true qualitatively rather than quantitatively, but even the word qualitatively needs qualification in that it should be interpreted on many occasions as implying the same type of process or condition without necessarily identicality of materials or other features. It would undoubtedly prove tedious to refer to this matter fully on each occasion that it is involved, but he who would try to assess the value of the many hypotheses put forward in geology should constantly bear it in mind. In addition to the question of uniformity other assumptions may be involved, tacitly or otherwise, and it is equally important to consider their validity or limitations wherever practicable.

Considerations of the above kind are in part the reason for the inclusion in the following text of numerical examples relating to various points. Qualitative discussion is not enough, and wherever possible quantitative or semi-quantitative studies must be attempted, for they lead to a better appreciation of the relative importance of the various factors involved in a given phenomenon. It may be considered that a numerical example constitutes a special case; but it illustrates a principle, and by drawing specific attention to some, at least, of the factors and assumptions involved, may in the end be of more value than sweeping generalizations or bald statements. The inclusion of these examples inevitably holds up the general discussion, but it is believed that this disadvantage is more than offset by the emphasis they place on the quantitative approach. It is following the same policy that some data have been presented in graphical or other form rather more fully than is absolutely essential for the immediate purpose, because these data may be of assistance in attempts to extend or modify some of the ideas discussed in the text.

Some observations which must be considered in connexion with the origin of petroleum

Commercial oilfields have been found in rocks ranging in age from Pre-Cambrian to Pleistocene. They are generally in rocks of marine origin. Oil production has been obtained at depths exceeding 17,000 ft. There is no reason to believe that this is the limit, and it must be recognized that, except possibly for off-shore fields, the accumulations now being exploited have been at appreciably greater depths than at present.

Oil is a fluid and is obtained from rocks in which fluid flow is possible. A number of features, noted in Chapter IV on Migration and Accumulation, strongly support the conclusion that the formation of an oil or gas accumulation has involved the flow and segregation of these substances. This flow adds to the difficulties of solving the problem of oil origin, because in many cases the hydrocarbons are thought to have moved out of the rocks in which they were formed, and in some instances the travel is believed to have been quite extensive. This mobility has to be considered in examining the deductions about the conditions of oil origin which may be drawn directly from the statements given in the previous paragraph.

Because of the imperfections in the knowledge concerning oil formation and concerning the other processes which are believed to be involved in the creation of an oil accumulation, it is necessary at times to make use of indirect evidence. This sometimes requires reference to matters which are logically discussed in detail later from the point of

view of the assumed sequence of events in the formation of a commercial oil accumulation, and in some cases savours of arguing in a circle.

Table VI presents figures on the estimated oil reserves (past production plus probable unproduced reserves) of the larger developed fields
in the various geological systems in the U.S.A.

Considerable volumes of oil reserves have been found yearly in the

TABLE VI

(After Hopkins,[21] with additions)

	Estimated reserves	Number of fields*	Age
	10^6 barrels		10^6 years
Pleistocene	1	1	
Pliocene	5,218	70	1
Miocene	7,337	410	14
Oligocene	6,048	410	31
Eocene	2,532	420	44
Cretaceous	10,064	730	60
Jurassic	779	110	125
Triassic	20	6	157
Permian	7,904	400	185
Carboniferous	13,474	3,570	223
Devonian	2,130	510	309
Silurian	544	105	354
Ordovician	4,267	825	381
Cambrian	59	55	448
Pre-Cambrian	3	3	553

* These figures exclude several thousand pools which are too small to be recorded
separately.

U.S.A. for nearly a century, and hence there is no reason to believe that
the above figures are very close to the amounts which will ultimately be
discovered. They may, however, in some instances be a rough guide to
the relative amounts which will eventually be found in the various
systems, but for a variety of reasons these figures may not be close to
the relative amounts *formed* in these systems. Much oil and gas may
have been formed and not aggregated into commercial accumulations,
or, where aggregation has occurred, have been lost by removal of the
reservoir rock or by escape from it via fractures or other avenues opened
by disturbance or erosion. Oil may have been formed in one system and
migrated into reservoir rocks in another system. Furthermore, the oil
recoverable by the usual methods is but a fraction of the total oil in the
reservoir rock, and reserve figures relate only to recoverable oil.

The various geological systems represent periods of time which differ considerably in length, and apart from this they are by no means identical as regards the palaeogeographical and depositional conditions which their rocks represent; indeed, the rocks in a single system may reveal marked differences in this last respect, both laterally and vertically.

Since there are no particular reasons for believing that, given certain conditions, potential oil-forming materials could not have been deposited in the rocks in each of the geological systems from the Cambrian to the Pleistocene, the presence of oilfields in the latter may be construed as showing that oil pools can be formed in a period of the order of one million years, unless in each of the pools in this system the oil has migrated from older formations. Because oil migration and accumulation may be quite slow processes (see Chapter IV), the time required for the formation of an oil pool may be considerably greater than that needed for the formation of oil.

Weeks[45] has stated that about half of the 185,000 million barrels of oil discovered to date occurs in carbonate rocks. He also notes that this type of rock is estimated to comprise only about 15–18 per cent. of all the sedimentary rocks. On this basis the incidence of proved oil occurrence is several times higher in carbonate rocks than in non-carbonate sediments. The limitations of a comparison of this nature must, however, be stressed. First, the quantity of oil is the estimated recoverable reserve, not the known oil in place (see also p. 2). Secondly, it is improbable that reserves to be discovered in the future will be small in comparison with the above figure or that they will necessarily be distributed in the different reservoir rock types in the same ratio as the past discoveries. Thirdly, had the Near East fields not been discovered (they are believed to account for nearly a quarter of the known recoverable oil), although the ratio of occurrence would still have been markedly in favour of the carbonate rocks, it would have been only a little more than half of the value obtained when all the presently known recoverable oil is used in the comparison.

Biochemical processes are known whereby methane is formed in quantity and in periods of time which are negligible geologically, and, except for the quantitative aspect, the same would appear to be true for some of the higher hydrocarbons which have been reported by Rawn, Banta, and Pomeroy[30] to be present in small amounts in gases obtained by the fermentation of sewage sludge (Table VII).

Appreciable amounts of ethane and of olefines have been reported in the gases occluded in coals.[15]

When the gases are pumped out of lump coal the higher hydrocarbons predominate in those given off at a late stage, but the total amount is small in comparison with the quantity of methane evolved when coal is freshly powdered.[14] Solvent extraction of coals has revealed the presence of heavy hydrocarbons, and pentacontane has been recognized in a Lancashire coal. It is not clear how far these heavy hydrocarbons are

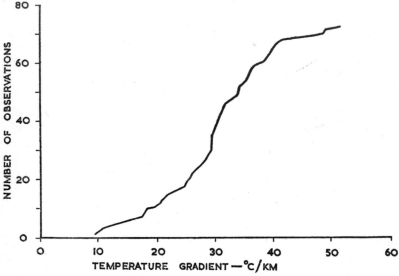

TABLE VII

(Rawn, Banta, and Pomeroy[30])

Composition of gas from sewage sludge			
	%		%
CH_4	67	H_2S	0·0004
CO_2	32	C_2H_6	0·04
CO	0·03	C_3H_8 and C_4H_{10}	0·01
H_2	0·04	C_5H_{12} and higher	0·07

FIG. 6. Cumulative curve based on data assembled by Spicer[35] for wells over 3,000 ft. deep.

original or have been formed during coalification of vegetable matter, because many terrestrial plants produce some hydrocarbons in their life processes. Numerous cases of the production of hydrocarbons in land plants have been listed by Brooks.[5] Living kelp is stated to contain heavy hydrocarbons, including cyclic forms, and the same is true of some freshwater algae. At certain stages in their life-cycle diatoms are reported to contain some globules of oil which are in part, at least, hydrocarbon in composition.

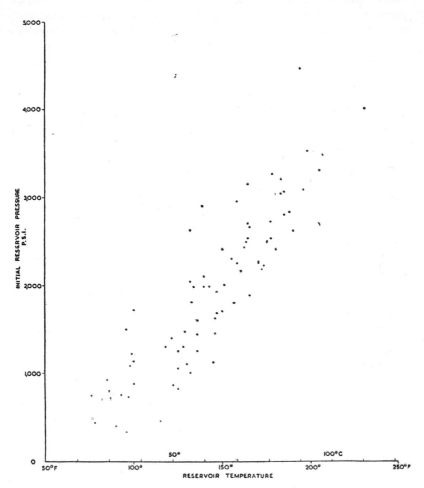

FIG. 7. Reservoir pressures and temperatures for various oilfields.

Conditions for oil formation

There are good reasons for expecting the mean pressure/depth gradient in sedimentary areas to be most commonly in the range 0·43–1·0 p.s.i./ft. (see Chapter V). The temperature/depth gradients in many sedimentary areas are in the range 0·0054–0·012° C./ft. (Fig. 6). These figures form a basis for estimating the order of magnitude of the temperature and pressure at a given depth. Fig. 7 shows a plot of some oilfield reservoir pressures and the associated temperatures. It seems unreasonable to expect that all oil accumulations have been buried as deeply as or even slightly more deeply than 17,892 ft., the depth of the present deepest oil production. The pressure at this depth might be 7,500 p.s.i. and the temperature 230° C. (using the hydrostatic gradient and the maximum temperature gradient given above). It may therefore be concluded that petroleum is formed at pressures, temperatures, and depths which are less than these values, and, indeed, Cox[9] has stated that the geological data suggest a *minimum* thickness of about 5,000 ft. of sediments for oil formation. (Some recent observations by Smith appear not to agree with this statement—see p. 37.) Cox notes that the associated temperature and pressure might be of the order of 65° C. and 2,000–5,000 p.s.i., respectively. The formation of 5,000 ft. of sediments would occupy a considerable time, but it is not possible to assign a figure to this which is more than a reasoned guess. Cox also remarks that there is 'no evidence . . . to prove that any petroleum has been formed since the Pliocene, although sedimentation patterns and thicknesses in Pleistocene and Recent sediments are similar to those in the Pliocene where petroleum has formed. The scale factor for time since the Pliocene cannot be reckoned accurately in calendar years, but may be taken for scale purposes as about a million years for the formation of the youngest known petroleum in geologic history.'

From a study of fossil sediments Schuchert has estimated the average rates of deposition since the beginning of Cambrian time to be as follows:

Sandstone	68 cm./1,000 years	
Shale	34 ,,	,,
Limestone	14 ,,	,,

In the deeper parts of the Clyde Sea Moore inferred the rate to be about 100 cm./1,000 years, while Strøm arrived at a figure of 27 cm./1,000 years for varved deposits in the stagnant Drammensfjord. Both these localities are in environments where rapid rates of sedimentation are to be expected. A rate of 5–6 cm./1,000 years has been given for the Black Sea and 19 cm./1,000 years for the Gulf of California. In each case allowance has been made for the high water content of recently formed fine sediments. Sverdrup, Johnson, and Fleming note that large local variations in the rate of deposition are to be expected, but that the scattered information suggests rates of accumulation of the order of 10 cm. of solid material in 1,000 years.

The preceding figures may be used to make a rough estimate of the time required for the formation of a thickness of 5,000 ft. of sediments, or of any other thickness that may be deemed relevant. Application of

Schuchert's figures gives lengths of time of two to four million years for the formation of 5,000 ft. of sandstones and shales, the precise figure depending on their proportions. These times are of the same order of magnitude as that indicated by Cox's direct statement.

The time, temperature, and pressure associated with a given thickness of sediments are all dependent to a considerable degree on that thickness, and hence, if a given depth of burial is necessary for the formation of petroleum, it is not possible from that knowledge alone to argue as to which of these factors is critical, or whether all are of importance in oil formation. In quoting 5,000 ft. of burial it seems most likely that Cox was referring to the formation of oil pools and not merely to the formation of oil. In the course of burial to this depth, clays and shales might have lost, by compaction, 90 per cent. of the water that would be lost during burial to 10,000 ft. (assuming that the compaction obeys Athy's law—see Fig. 37). It is therefore evident that for oil formed when the burial reached 5,000 ft., a considerable proportion would probably fail to be transferred to a reservoir rock by fluid movements associated with compaction. This point will be discussed in detail later.

It is also a temptation to suggest that rocks which act as effective cap-rocks at 5,000 ft. or less would not be capable of allowing the passage of hydrocarbons to form an accumulation when they were near the state of compaction in which they would be at that depth, However, it has to be recognized that compaction probably does continue at greater depths, and that the efficacy of these rocks as seals may be in some measure dependent on the state of aggregation of the hydrocarbons in an oil or gas accumulation.

If thickness of sediment is critical in oil formation, i.e. via temperature or pressure, oil will be formed more quickly in areas of rapid sedimentation such as geosynclinal troughs than on the more stable forelands. Holmes[20] has tabulated figures on rates of sedimentation, and these suggest that the maximum rates have increased with the passage of time. If true this would possibly imply, if thicknesses of sediments are significant, more rapid oil formation in late than in early times, other things being equal.

Some crude oils contain chlorophyll porphyrins. These complex compounds are stated to be oxidized readily and to break down at temperatures above 200° C. If the porphyrins were with the organic matter from which the oil was formed, they show that the conditions were anaerobic, otherwise they would have been oxidized, and that the crude has never been at temperatures in excess of about 200° C. It has, however, sometimes been suggested that these compounds have been picked up by the oil during migration. In this case their indications about anaerobic conditions cannot be applied without independent check to the oil at the time it was formed; but unless the oil has migrated upwards through a very considerable thickness of sediments before picking up the porphyrins, they will still fix a rough upper limit for the temperature of oil formation.

It is generally believed that shales or clays are the commonest oil source rocks, but it is admitted that there are cases where the evidence suggests that a limestone was the source rock.

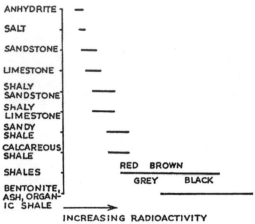

FIG. 8. Range of relative radio-activity of sedimentary rocks.

The radio-activity of sedimentary rocks varies widely, shales and clays being usually the most radio-active, while limestones, particularly the purer types, are low in radio-activity (Fig. 8). This property is of interest in connexion with the suggestions which have been made that radio-activity aids the transformation of organic matter to petroleum. The source of the radio-activity in these sediments has usually not been defined, but it appears that some of it is due to potassium, while the more intensely radio-active elements contribute varying amounts of activity. The experimental work on the formation of hydrocarbons by radio-activity has employed the more active elements. How far the less active elements will give comparable results, though in a longer time, has not been indicated; i.e. is it correct to assume that the activities, as measured conventionally by Geiger-Muller, scintillation, or other counters, are a true indication of the relative capacities of the different radio-active elements to cause certain reactions in other materials?

It has been stated that prolific oil production is invariably associated with areas of thick and rapidly accumulated sediments, such as are typical of orogenic belts. Nevertheless, the sediments formed in the relatively shallow seas which spread widely as a result of epeirogeny also have given rise to oil, but the oil pools are usually smaller according to Stebinger.[36] A study of the distribution of oilfields shows clear evidence of a common association with geosynclines. But this must not be taken solely as an association with orogenic belts in the sense of fold zones. Admittedly many oilfields have been found in the foothills of such fold zones, and others have been lost by erosion or through the dislocations existing in the more intensely folded areas. However, important oilfields occur in the foreland areas where warping or arching is feeble.

Oil source material

The universal association of oilfields with sedimentary areas indicates that petroleum is formed in sediments. The non-organic components of sediments, other than possibly the carbonates, could not be the source of petroleum, while the carbonates do not constitute a very promising starting-point for the synthesis of organic compounds in sediments.*

Hence it appears most reasonable to assume that petroleum is generated basically from organic matter incorporated in the sediments in the course of their formation. The waters from which the sub-aqueous sediments are deposited commonly support both plant and animal life, whether the sediments are marine, brackish, or freshwater. These organisms are likely to be the main original source of the organic matter which is ultimately transformed into petroleum. There may, however, be some organic matter, from rivers or swamps, which reaches the body of water in which sedimentation takes place, and therefore has not developed in the water overlying the sediments.

Some of the observed differences in the composition of crude oils may be due to differences in the parent organic matter; others may be due to differences in the environments or conditions under which the transformation to petroleum and any subsequent evolution took place. Differences due to the former cause may be the result of differences in the types of organisms or their proportions; they may also be dependent in some degree upon the stages through which the organic matter passes from the time it ceases to live and until it is incorporated in the

---

* At first sight the work of Sisler and Zobell[38] might appear to cast doubt on this statement, since they state that carbonates, bicarbonates, and carbon dioxide can act as hydrogen acceptors, some hydrocarbon material being formed (see p. 60). However, the most likely source of the hydrogen is the bacterial decomposition of organic matter, although theoretically there could be other possibilities.

sediments. There may also be differences arising from other processes such as 'weathering', reaction with saline waters, &c. There are no known differences in the composition of crude oils which have been attributed with certainty solely or generally to the age of the oil. Low forms of life are commonly believed to show less change with time than do higher forms, and thus it may be argued that the former have contributed most to the formation of oil, because seemingly similar oils have been found in rocks of widely different ages.

The oils of the Rock sand, 50 ft. above the Burbank sand at Haverhill, and of the Bartlesville sand, 100 ft. below the Burbank sand, differ from the Burbank sand oils.[27] All three sands have had similar depths of burial and are similar in their relationships to regional structure. Hence the differences in these oils most likely arise from differences in the source materials, in the environments of deposition, or in the conditions of transformation.

Weeks[45] has stated that there is commonly a progressive change in oil composition at right-angles to the flank trend of the basins, and an increase in A.P.I. gravity with depth in the corresponding deposition basin.

A plant or part of one may be incorporated in the sediments directly, and the same is true of an animal. On the other hand, each, while living or dead, could be consumed by an animal, part of its substance being transformed into the living substance of the consuming organism and the rest being excreted. The excrement will consist of the more resistant parts of the food together with waste products formed as a result of metabolism in the living animal. It is therefore possible for resistant substances to reach the sediments directly or indirectly. When conditions permit the existence of bottom-living organisms (other than bacteria) which feed on the bottom deposits, organic matter in those deposits may pass through animals a number of times before it is finally entombed. Even before final entombment in the sediments bacteria may act upon the organic matter. Hence it seems that a series of organisms, both macroscopic and microscopic, may by one means or another cause changes whereby the make-up of the organic matter entombed in the sediments differs from the organic matter in the living organisms.

A relatively small number of studies have been made of the organic matter in recent sediments, and some of the data have been summarized by Trask.[39]

Tables VIII, IX, and X provide analytical data on a few types of organisms, and averaged figures for the organic matter in some sediments. Table VIII gives the elemental analyses with some figures on

TABLE VIII

(After Trask, with additions)

	Percentage composition of organic matter by weight				Ratio of organic matter to carbon	Ratio of carbon to hydrogen
	Carbon	Nitrogen	Hydrogen	Oxygen		
Peridineans* .	45	3	7	45	2·2	6·4
Diatoms . .	50	6	8	36	2·0	6·25
Copepods† .	50	10	8	32	2·0	6·25
Marine sapropel	52	11	6	30	1·9	8·7
Recent marine sediments .	56	6	8	30	1·8	7·0
Lithified sediments . .	64	4	9	23	1·6	7·1
Petroleum (Chap. II, Table III) .	83–86·5	..	11–14·2	..	1·16–1·2	6·02–7·55
Methane . .	75	..	25	..	1·33	3·0
$C_{40}H_{82}$ . .	85·4	..	14·6	..	1·17	5·85

* Peridineans are planktonic.   † Copepods are small crustacea.

TABLE IX

(After Brandt and Trask)

	Crude protein	Ether extract*	Carbohydrates	Crude fibre
	%	%	%	%
Peridineans . .	14	1.5	85?	?
Diatoms† . . .	29	8	63	0
Copepods . . .	65	8	22	0
Higher invertebrates .	70	10	20	0
Organic matter in marine sediments . .	40	1	47	0

* The ether extract includes any fats present.
† The fat content of the organisms varies with the stage of life and the environmental conditions.

petroleum and methane for comparison. Inspection of Table VIII shows that the ratios of carbon to hydrogen for the various types of organisms, and the organic matter of recent and ancient sediments, fall within the range of the values of the same ratio for petroleum. The ratio for marine sapropel is rather higher. Strictly the comparison should be with crude oil, the associated hydrocarbon gas and any asphaltic matter which may have been precipitated from the oil. The over-all gas : oil ratios at present found in oilfields vary considerably, and the information published is

TABLE X

(After Waksman and others, and Trask)

	Phyto-plankton*	Zoo-plankton	Marine sediments	Ancient marine sediments
	%	%	%	%
Ether extract†	2	10	1	3
Alcohol extract‡	9	5	5	4
Water extract§	2·3	5	3	3
Hemicellulose	11	0	2	
Cellulose	5	2	1	0
Pentosans	29	0	7¶	6?
Urionic acid	16	0	..	..
Acid-insoluble non-nitrogenous compounds‖	5	3	31	48
Protein	7	56**	40	27
Water-soluble	..	..	1	1
Acid-soluble	..	..	19	4
Acid-insoluble	..	..	17	15
Ash	14	13	?	..

* Average analyses of three types of organisms: *Fucus vesicularis, Platycarpus,* and *Ulna lactuca.*

† Includes oils, fats, pigments, organic sulphur compounds, and sulphur.

‡ Includes waxes, resins, pigments, and alkaloids.

§ Includes sugars, starches, simple alcohols, and simple organic acids and their salts and esters (and possibly also some protein for phyto- and zoo-plankton, but not for the marine sediments).

‖ Includes lignin.

¶ Acid-soluble non-nitrogenous substances except hemi-cellulose.

** Includes 6 per cent. chitin.

insufficient to select the average values or the limiting values. Moreover, these need not be the original values. However, in order to obtain some guidance on the effects of making allowance for the associated gas, two cases have been examined. In the first, the over-all gas: oil ratio was assumed to be 500 cu. ft./brl., and in the second 2,000 cu. ft./brl. The former yielded carbon/hydrogen ratios ranging about 5·0 to 7·1 and the latter 5·5 to 6·4. In the present state of knowledge it is not practicable to make a general allowance for any precipitated asphaltic matter. Such an allowance would raise the value of the ratio.

The principal difference between the elemental composition of the different forms of organic matter and petroleum is the deficiency of oxygen and nitrogen in the latter. This does not necessarily mean that the organic matter converted to petroleum loses only these elements in the process; some carbon and hydrogen are probably lost in combination with the nitrogen and/or oxygen.

In Table IX the proportions of the main types of compounds in the various groups of organisms are shown, together with figures for the higher invertebrates and marine sediments. Table X presents the results of more detailed analyses, averaged for certain members of the phytoplankton and zoo-plankton, and also for recent and ancient marine sediments. Comment on the implications of the data tabulated will be made later at appropriate points.

Rankama[28] has tabulated the ratios of the C^{12} and C^{13} isotopes for

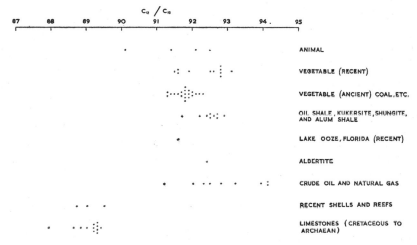

FIG. 9. Ratios of $C^{12}:C^{13}$ in various materials (after Rankama[28]).

carbon in various materials. The lower limits of this ratio for carbon of vegetable origin and carbon in petroleum are almost identical, while the range for carbon of animal origin has a rather lower limit (Fig. 9). However, there are only a few determinations for animal carbon, and the general reliability of the data is not sufficiently high, while the observations are not sufficiently numerous to use the differences in range to prove a preponderant vegetable contribution to the source material of petroleum.

Trask and Wu[41] analysed a number of recent marine sediments in an attempt to determine whether petroleum forms at the time of deposition of the sediments. The carbon tetrachloride extracts were examined (Table XI).

It was concluded that no liquid hydrocarbons were present. The paraffines comprised solid hydrocarbons and possibly wax-like substances. The content of fatty acids may be greater than shown, because the calcium or magnesium soaps would not be soluble in carbon

TABLE XI

(Based on Trask)

	Florida Bay	Channel Is. California	Pamlico Sound	Florida algal lake
	Parts per 10,000			
Free sulphur . . .	22	51	104	97
Caproic acid . . .	1	..	..	..
Melissic acid ⎫ Montanic acid ⎬ · . .	1	5	..	..
Cerotic acid . . .	..	..	6	16
Sulphur compounds . .	30 ⎫	8	⎧ 30	36
Pigments	5 ⎬		⎩ 5	4
Cholesterol . . .	..	trace	..	2
Phytosterol . . .	0.2	..	..	16
Paraffines	6	23	trace	68
Total extract . . .	65	87	146	238

tetrachloride. The phytosterol and cholesterol point, respectively, to the organic matter including substances of vegetable and animal origin.

Other studies of a comparable nature have been made by Wells and Erickson.[46] The material examined was a recent sandy sediment with some mud obtained from shallow water in Chincoteague Bay, Virginia. The organic matter formed 0·7 per cent. of the sediment, and the substances recognized include chlorophyll, cholesterol, sulphur, 'algin', wax, humic acid material soluble in alcohol and humic acid material insoluble in alcohol, fatty acid material, pentosans, and acid-soluble organic matter. These substances did not necessarily occur in the free state in the sediments. It is believed that some of the 'humic acids' and fatty acids occurred as calcium or magnesium salts. The waxes had melting-points in the range 25°–90° C.

Gas, presumed to be methane, oil, and wax have been noted in comparatively large quantities in the sediments of two freshwater lakes (Lake Allequash and Grassy Lake) by Twenhofel and McElvey.[42] Oil and wax soluble in ether and chloroform were reported to amount to 20 gal./ton of dried sediment. These materials were thought to have been derived from diatoms, fatty algae, animals, and perhaps some of the higher plants, but some might have been formed by bacterial alteration of non-fatty organic matter. Comparable observations were made in the sediments of Little Long (Hiawatha) Lake, Wisconsin, but in both cases the nature of the oil was not determined.[43]

Lovely has drawn attention to the fact that oil indications of a waxy nature in the Middle Coal Measures of England may be linked with the common occurrences of cannel coal in these measures.[24] The cannels are formed from spores, pollen exines, and cuticles of vegetation, and these are predominantly waxy and fatty in composition. Furthermore, the Lower Cretaceous oil indications are associated with typical fresh-water beds, and the Upper Jurassic beds, in which bituminous residues are common, constitute a predominantly freshwater section. Oil has been reported elsewhere in freshwater deposits. Hence this type of deposit must not be ignored provided that it satisfies certain conditions, even though marine sediments seem to have provided most oil. This state of affairs may be the result of the formation *and preservation* of greater amounts of suitable marine sediments than of suitable fresh-water sediments.

Trask and his co-workers have consistently failed to find significant amounts of liquid hydrocarbons in the recent sediments which they have examined, and therefore concluded that the formation of petroleum does not take place early in the history of the sediments. However, some years ago Zobell, Grant, and Haas[54] drew attention to the existence of various bacteria which can destroy hydrocarbons and to their occurrence in marine deposits. Zobell has suggested that the activities of such bacteria on samples, between the time of collection and the time of analysis, might be an explanation of Trask's failure to find liquid hydrocarbons in recent sediments. In support of his suggestion Zobell quoted an instance in which the sample immediately after collection contained 10–20 mgm. of liquid hydrocarbons per 100 gm., but much of this had disappeared a few days later.

It has been apparent for a number of years that the best chances of gaining information about the origin of petroleum might lie in the in-vestigation of cores from wells drilled offshore, and recently a brief note has been published by Smith[33] in which there is a description of the recovery, from cores, of liquid aliphatic and aromatic hydrocarbons similar to those found in crude oil.

Details are given for cores taken at depths of 3–4 ft., 18–22 ft., and 102–3 ft. below the floor of the Gulf of Mexico at a point about 7 miles off Grande Island, Louisiana. The cores are described as consisting of grey silty clay, in places interbedded with grey fine-grained silty sand. The samples were dried under reduced pressure, very finely pulverized, and extracted with a special mixture of organic solvents. Subsequently the residue left by evaporation of the solvent was separated by chroma-tography on alumina. In all cases paraffine-naphthene, aromatic, and asphaltic fractions were obtained by elution, but a large proportion of the extracted organic matter was too tightly sorbed by the alumina to be eluted by conventional solvents. Elemental analyses, infra-red absorption spectra, and the behaviour on the alumina during chromatographic separation are stated to have proved that the paraffine-naphthene and aromatic fractions are actually hydrocarbons.

The figures of Table XII suggest a progressive change in the direction of petroleum with increased burial. Clearly the pressure and temperature to which the material of these cores has been submitted will have been low, far below the figures indicated by Cox as being critical, while geo-

TABLE XII

(After Smith[33])

Sample	Grammes of organic matter extracted per 100 gm. of dried sediment	Chromatographic analysis of extracted organic matter			
		Per cent. paraffine-naphthene	Per cent. aromatic	Per cent. asphaltic	Per cent. remaining on alumina
3–4 ft. .	0·031	6·0	1·5	14·0	78·5
18–22 ft. .	0·032	17·9	2·5	12·1	67·5
102–103 ft. .	0·031	25·0	5·7	10·6	58·7

logically the time for the formation of the hydrocarbons will have been short. The data presented are insufficient to show whether the process is nearing completion, and there is no reference to the total content of organic matter in the cores. The deepest core contained about 0·013 gm. of paraffine-naphthene, aromatic, and asphaltic material per 100 gm. of dried sediment.

In the absence of information on the ratio of the extractable matter to the total organic content, it is impossible to decide whether the constancy of the amount of extractable matter for the three cores (about 0·031 gm./100 gm. of dried sediment) is significant. If the ratio of extractable matter to total organic matter in the samples is increasing, it might be assumed that there is increased generation of extractable matter in addition to changes in the composition of the extractable matter. However, extrapolation of the data of Table XII merely indicates that the maximum yield of paraffine, naphthene, aromatic, and asphaltic compounds could not exceed 0·031 gm./100 gm. of dried sediment, *if* they are being produced from the substance retained on the alumina and if that substance itself is no longer being formed.

If it is accepted that Smith's findings mean what they appear to mean it is evident that petroleum formation takes place at substantially lower pressures, at lower temperatures, in shorter periods of time, and at smaller depths of burial than were indicated by Cox.

The descriptions of Smith's observations do not indicate whether the cores gave evidence of the presence of gaseous hydrocarbons. They do not record whether the cores showed any radio-activity or contained live bacteria. Information on the porosities of the cores would also have been of interest provided that the method of coring did not disturb the original condition of the sediments. Experimental evidence on the production of methane, carbon dioxide, and hydrogen sulphide is satisfactory, but it would be of interest to know whether these gases were observed in the cores. The presence or absence of hydrogen would be a further point of interest. To what extent the spread of compounds in the three main groups given in Table XII corresponds with the spread in crude petroleum is not apparent from the brief published note. It is therefore not possible to indicate whether or not further evolution or other processes would be necessary to convert the substances found into a typical crude petroleum.

Zobell[53] has given an estimate, based on laboratory studies, that an average of ten bacteria in 1 c.c. of sediment could produce 0·001 gm. of 'unsaponifiable, ether-soluble, oil-like material' in $1·6 \times 10^8$ years. If 1 c.c. of the sediment weighed 1·5–2·0 gm. and had an average content of 10,000 bacteria, application of the above rate indicates that each gramme of sediment would yield 0·001 gm. of this oil-like material in about 3×10^5 years. In estimating the probable amount of organic matter converted into petroleum at Santa Fe Springs, California, Trask[38] concluded that the most likely yield was about 0·0012 gm. of oil per gramme of sediment, the accumulated oil amounting to some 0·00053 gm./gm. of sediment. Both estimated yields are subject to a considerable degree of uncertainty (in particular, the figure of 10,000 bacteria per gramme was a guess made before the comparison with the Santa Fe yield was made), but if their general similarity is more than a coincidence it seems reasonable to infer that the formation of oil in commercially significant amounts may not require a time which is geologically long. The period of time computed above is well within the minimum period of a million years suggested by Cox for oil (presumably oilfield) formation. Oil formation within this time would make primary migration possible at a geologically early date and provide appreciable time for both primary and secondary migration within the minimum time suggested by Cox.

Until more information is available on the amount of organic matter in the cores examined by Smith it is difficult to compare the indicated oil production with the meagre published views on the possible amount of oil generated in sediments associated with oilfields. The present oil content is about a tenth, while the total extractable organic matter of the deepest core is about a quarter of what Trask considered to be the most probable oil yield of the source sediments of the Santa Fe Springs field. These figures, as a whole, do not seem incompatible, since the productivity of source rocks may reasonably be expected to show considerable variations.

It may also be noted that in their studies of the bitumen content of sediments Trask and Patnode[40] found an average of 0·00055 gm. of bitumen per gramme of sediment, which figure was close to the 0·0006 gm./gm. found in their work on recent sediments.

Amount and distribution of organic matter in sediments

Trask and his co-workers have published information on the amounts of organic matter in sediments, both ancient and modern. In many cases the organic matter was not determined directly, but was obtained by making some analytically simpler operation, such as measuring the nitrogen or organic carbon content and multiplying by a factor to convert the result to the equivalent amount of organic matter. However, the conversion factors are not constant, with the result that the derived figures for organic matter are subject to a measure of uncertainty. Trask and Patnode[40] state that the factor for converting organic carbon assays to organic matter for sediments in the vicinity of oilfields 'cannot be less than 1·2 or more than 2·0, and probably ranges mainly between 1·4 and 1·8'. A convenient factor seems to be about 1·6.

Because of the limitations of the methods used in estimating the organic content of large numbers of samples, it is clear that the figures obtained by these methods could, in some instances, be of widely different significance in relation to the problem of oil formation. The methods, as indicated above, do not characterize the organic matter, but assume over-all similarity in the different samples and a reasonably constant relation of the organic matter to the particular substance measured directly. This assumption may be justifiable in general when the specimens are indicative of similar environments of deposition.

The degree of constancy in the make-up of the original organic matter, in the make-up of the organic matter now remaining in the sediments or in the relations of the latter, as a bulked quantity, to the amount of oil formed, is a matter for speculation.

The determinations made by Trask and his associates, either directly or indirectly, showed the organic matter of recent sediments to range from 0·3 per cent. for deep sea oozes up to 7 per cent. for the Channel Islands region of California.[37] Some Black Sea deposits contained as much as 35 per cent. of organic matter. The average organic content of all the recent sediments examined was 2·5 per cent. His studies of ancient sediments showed 38 per cent. to have less than 1 per cent. of organic matter, 33 per cent. had 1–2 per cent., 12 per cent. had 2–3 per cent., 10 per cent. had 3–5 per cent., and 4 per cent. had over 5 per cent.; the general average organic content was about 1·5 per cent. Trask and Patnode have stated that:

The organic content of ancient sediments ranges from 0·2 to 10%; but fewer than one-tenth of the samples studied contain less than 0·4% organic matter, and equally few have more than 5% organic matter. . . . The California deposits are richest, and the Appalachian sediments are the leanest, but rich and lean layers of sediments are found in all regions. The organic content may be practically constant throughout several thousand feet of strata, as in the Knoxville formation in northern California; or it may vary considerably within a fraction of an inch, as in some of the Miocene beds in the Los Angeles Basin. The organic content in individual stratigraphic zones may be essentially the same throughout an area 200 miles in diameter, as in the upper part of the Niobrara formation in Wyoming; or it may increase 1% (on the basis of total weight of the sediment) within a distance of less than 2 miles, as in some of the Miocene deposits in the Los Angeles Basin.[40]

In the ancient sediments the organic content might be largely a residue or material not capable at any time of yielding oil in the sediments, i.e.

TABLE XIII

(After Zobell[50])

Deposit	Median diameter of particles	Nitrogen content	Water content	Bacteria per gramme (wet basis)
	μ	%	%	
Sand	50–100	0·09	33	22,000
Silt	5–50	0·19	56	78,000
Clay	1–5	0·37	82	390,000
Colloid	< 1	1·0	98	1,510,000

it is not necessarily correct to assume that it is a measure of past oil-forming capacity.

For recent sands, silts, and clays the relative amounts of organic matter were about 1:2:4 for a given surface supply. The bacterial content and certain other properties of recent sediments show qualitatively a generally similar behaviour.

It is probable that the increased number of bacteria in the finer sediments is related to the increased organic content.

In general terms the absolute quantity (not the amount relative to the mineral matter) of organic matter added to the sediments is dependent on the quantity of organisms living in the surface layers of the water. Although these organisms may not be incorporated in the sediments directly they form the food for other creatures, and so ultimately fix the amount of living substance developed in an area. The proportion of organic matter in the sediments depends on the relative rates of supply of mineral matter and organic matter.

The finer the mineral grains of a sediment the stiller must be the water for those grains to reach the bottom. Similarly, the finer or the less dense the particles of organic matter the stiller must be the water for them to be deposited. Thus it appears that the conditions which favour the sedimentation of fine mineral grains will also favour the deposition of minute organisms or fragments of organic matter. In this way the relatively high proportion of organic matter deposited with the finer sediments is partially explained, because the surface supply of organic matter may be fairly uniform over a considerable area relatively near shore, while the abundance of mineral matter may in some instances decrease with increased fineness.

A further factor involved is the preservation of organic matter in the sediments. Stebinger[36] has suggested that in waters less than about 50 fathoms deep, wave and tide action, oxidation, and scavengers create conditions unfavourable for the preservation of organic matter. If the water is still it will have a low content of dissolved oxygen, and this anaerobic condition presumably largely precludes the presence of bottom-living animals which feed on the organic matter in the sediments (see p. 29), and also prevents the existence of aerobic bacteria. The latter have a vigorous action on organic matter, breaking it down relatively rapidly to such simple substances as carbon dioxide, methane, and hydrogen. Under the conditions with little or no dissolved oxygen in the water there will be only anaerobic bacteria, and although these will attack the organic matter their action is not so intensive as that of the aerobic bacteria. They will reduce the combined oxygen content of the organic matter upon which they act, leaving the residue or products, in bulk composition at least, more nearly like petroleum (see Table VIII). Hence the anaerobic conditions which are associated with still water mean that the organic matter is less likely to be completely destroyed by bacteria than would be the case in more aerated water, and this is a second factor which contributes to the presence of relatively greater amounts of organic matter in fine than in coarse sediments, because coarse sediments signify agitated and therefore aerated water. Anaerobic conditions are marked by foetid hydrogen sulphide-bearing deposits.

The phyto-plankton, the plant organisms of the illuminated surface layers of the seas, provide the basic organic matter for the development of other organisms, and require for their own growth certain mineral nutrients. These nutrients are more abundant relatively near shore, or where there is upwelling of deep waters, than in mid-ocean. In the former circumstances the mineral nutrients are evidently being supplied from the land by rivers and streams. Consequently, the organic content of the waters is greater relatively near shore than in mid-ocean, with the corollary that the organic matter-bearing sediments which may be potential oil source rocks are more likely to be formed in the former than in the latter environment. From the point of view of forming oilfields a near-shore environment provides the possibility of other favourable conditions, namely, the interlayering or proximity of potential source and reservoir rocks.

Trask's observations support the preceding arguments (he states that although the organic content varies greatly in different regions it is fairly constant for about 100 miles off shore, but it decreases rapidly beyond this point, falling to insignificant amounts at 200–500 miles off shore). His observations also show that in relatively near-shore environments the amounts of organic matter in the sediments and also the sediments themselves are influenced by the submarine topography. In the depressions or basins the organic content of the sediments is greater than on the surrounding elevations, and there are also differences of mineral grain size, with the former features having the finer sediments. Undoubtedly the stiller and more stagnant waters of the depressions account for this state of affairs.

Recently Brongersma-Sanders[4] has suggested that the organic matter of source rocks may be explained not so much by stagnant conditions as by excessive development of plankton depleting the waters of certain nutrients and presumably, in essence, overpopulating the area with a certain group of organisms which on death rain upon the sea floor in abundance because of the absence of destructive agents. These hypertrophic conditions are said to occur in inland seas, in partly shut-off seas, and in some areas of upwelling. They are associated with mass mortality of invertebrates and vertebrates.

The agent of oil formation

Three agents have received extensive consideration with regard to the formation of petroleum. These are bacteria, radio-activity, and mild thermal metamorphism aided by pressure and time. Although it is convenient to discuss the mechanism of oil generation in terms of each of these separately, it must be recognized that to a large extent the arguments have usually been about the dominant mechanism, and therefore various combinations of these mechanisms have, in fact, been visualized on many occasions: (a) preliminary biochemical action yielding material which then undergoes a major change, caused by heat or radio-activity, to give petroleum; and (b) dominantly biochemical transformation with some modification or evolution of the resultant petroleum by thermal or pressure action, or by radio-activity.

Before considering each agent in detail it is necessary to note some general points. Firstly, there seem to be sound reasons for favouring a mechanism which would complete oil formation geologically early in the history of the source rocks.

If, as is argued later in Chapter IV on Migration and Accumulation, the transfer of oil from the source rock to the reservoir rock (in cases where these are not the same rock) is associated with compaction, then the earlier oil is formed the easier it is for it to move to the reservoir rock. In some cases the structural history of the oil accumulations or the absence of oil in certain structures points to early migration, and hence to early oil formation.

If compaction is the agent which causes the transfer of oil from a source rock to a reservoir rock, the influence of time of oil formation on the proportion transferred can be examined. The examination has been made in terms of the following simple assumptions: (a) the virgin oil moves at the same rate as the water being expelled by compaction (any lag will reduce the 'efficiency' of transfer); and (b) no water is entering the source rock section under consideration from external sources (such water entry would be expected to increase the 'efficiency' of transfer). For a given source rock series it can then be shown that the proportion of the oil transferred will increase as the final depth of burial increases, the depth of burial for oil formation being fixed. On the other hand, for a given source rock series and final depth of burial the proportion of the oil transferred diminishes as the depth of burial for oil formation increases. Fig. 10 summarizes the results of some of the approximate calculations made in terms of the above assumptions for a source rock series of 500 m. reduced thickness.*

The curve for a 250-m. (reduced) thick source rock section is essentially the same as for the 500-m. (reduced) thick section when its base is finally at a depth of 4,000 m. (reduced). There are large differences in the proportion transferred, and hence conversely, other things being

---

* The reduced thickness is the thickness to which the actual rock column would be reduced on compaction to zero porosity (see Appendix I).

equal, there will be wide variations in the amount of oil left behind in the source rock as the depth of burial for oil formation changes. Early oil formation will leave only a little oil in the source rock; late oil formation will leave much oil in the source rock for the same final depth of burial. Whether or not any oil left in the source rock will be detectable by conventional methods using solvents depends on that oil not having been converted later into something which is insoluble.

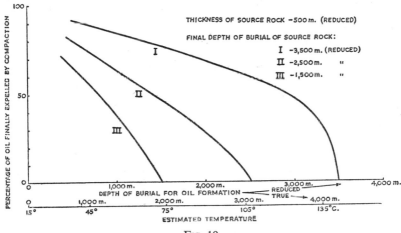

Fig. 10.

For the three main agents proposed for the transformation of organic matter to oil it seems logical to accept the following:

(*a*) *Bacteria*. This agent would most likely be active soon after deposition of the sediments and would probably complete the transformation in a geologically short time. There do not seem to be any good reasons for assuming any marked delay in the initiation of the complex series of reactions which would undoubtedly be involved in the biochemical formation of oil.

(*b*) *Radio-activity*. Radio-activity might be expected to cause oil formation at an early date in the history of the sediments, but the rate of transformation might be low, with the consequence that a long time would be required for the formation of substantial amounts of oil. The rate might diminish a little with time.

(*c*) *Heat*. If a critical temperature must be attained before this agent could begin to operate there would be delay in the start of oil formation until burial gave the required temperature. Thereafter further burial would accelerate the rate of transformation. Alternatively, if no critical temperature is needed to start the reactions, there would be very slow transformation at first, but the rate would increase progressively as the depth of burial, and with it the temperature, increased. Thus the main phase of oil formation might occur relatively long, geologically, after deposition of the source rock.

In terms of these suggestions, and assuming that oil once formed remains capable of extraction by solvents, transformation by heat ought to leave more 'oil' in the source rock than biochemical transformation, other things being equal; radio-active transformation might be intermediate between these limits so far as extractable oil left in the source rock is concerned.

It is not known whether when the transforming agent has become active all the organic matter capable of yielding hydrocarbons is changed to oil and gas. In the case of heat it would seem that when the appropriate conditions have been attained all the suitable organic matter will in time be changed to oil. The same would probably be true for radioactivity, but for bacteria conditions can be visualized under which transformation would cease before all the suitable organic matter had been changed to oil. Greater knowledge of the nature of the organic matter in rocks would clearly be of value in various respects. Uncertainties such as that noted on page 40 might then be cleared up.

Although the preceding discussion indicates some of the features which would be associated with various possible means of oil formation, existing knowledge does not appear to be adequate to use these features in order to get an indication of the nature of the effective agent of oil formation. The amount of oil formed would presumably be dependent, among other things, on the quantity and detailed make-up of the original organic matter. Until it is practicable to distinguish between organic matter which is a residue from oil formation, any capable of being converted into oil, and that which is unrelated to oil formation, it is doubtful whether the ratio of extractable oil to total organic matter would necessarily be of critical significance.

It has been noted earlier that the virgin oil content of a source rock may be small, possibly of the order of one part in a thousand, and it may be associated with perhaps 10–20 times its own weight of other organic matter. These figures draw attention to the nature and difficulty of the problem.

Trask and Patnode[40] have tabulated data on the 'bitumen' and organic contents (via the organic carbon and nitrogen contents) of ancient sediments (*Source beds of petroleum*, Tables 104, 123, and 142), and give average values for certain formations ranging Cambrian to Eocene in age. The 'bitumen' contents listed ranged 0·00–0·24 per cent., but there is no information to show what proportion of the observed bitumen content is indigenous to the rocks.

Thermal transformation

The hypothesis of the thermal transformation of organic matter to petroleum is based on observations of two main types. First, coals, lignites, oil shales, vegetable matter, and oils or fats of vegetable and animal origin, when heated to suitable temperatures undergo decomposition, with the production of oily or tarry matter, gases, and other substances. Decompositions of this type are carried out industrially and in the laboratory at temperatures well over 300° C. and commonly in the range 500°–700° C. By fractionation and other treatment the oily or tarry material can be made to yield products which in some respects resemble fractions obtained by distilling crude oil. Engler,[19] and Warren and Storer,[44] carried out thermal decomposition of menhaden fish oil and of the soaps of this oil, respectively, in investigations of the origin of petroleum. Engler fractionated his basic product, and one cut, after treatment with acid and caustic soda, was stated to resemble kerosene. Since Engler carried out his experiments in an autoclave the decomposition took place under pressure (about 220 p.s.i.), the temperature being 320°–400° C. With reference to the basic material used by Warren and Storer, it should be noted that appreciable amounts of the soaps of fatty acids are believed to occur in the sediments (see p. 35). In attempting to visualize the entire process of petroleum formation from fish, Engler postulated the early breakdown of the proteins and hydrolysis of the fats before their thermal decomposition.

With any of the materials mentioned above, the products of thermal decomposition, industrially or in the laboratory, depend in some measure on the temperature and other conditions applied, but the basic product always contains substantial amounts of compounds best described as 'unsaturateds'. In this respect it differs markedly from crude petroleum. In a general way the lower the temperature of decomposition the greater the proportion of paraffin-type hydrocarbons in the basic product. High temperatures tend to give considerable amounts of the benzene type of hydrocarbon.

Secondly, in the course of investigations on certain oil shales Maier and Zimmerly[25] observed that the lower the temperature used in the thermal treatment the longer the time needed to generate a given amount of extractable 'bitumen' in the shale. The temperatures they employed ranged 275°–365° C., and the times were up to 144 hours. From their observations they derived a relationship between temperature, time of heating, and the amount of 'bitumen' produced, and this relationship was then used to predict the time required to produce a given amount of 'bitumen' at lower temperatures than those employed in the experiments. Maier and Zimmerly concluded that a 1 per cent. conversion of the organic matter in the oil shale to 'bitumen' would require 8.4×10^5 years at 100° C. Trask reviewed Maier and Zimmerly's data and stated that the times for 1 per cent. conversion to 'bitumen' should be 8.4×10^4 years at 100° C., and 6.7×10^7 years at 60° C. Qualitatively similar results were obtained by Trask when recent organic sediments were thermally decomposed.

The laboratory and industrial thermal decompositions carried out at temperatures of several hundred degrees centigrade proceed rapidly, and any mineral matter associated with the organic matter shows clear evidence of having been raised to a high temperature. Except for a few rare cases where sediments with organic matter have been thermally altered by igneous intrusions, the sediments of interest from the point of view of petroleum do not show signs of having been subjected to high temperatures. Inspection of Fig. 6 indicates that the earth's temperature gradients will not yield temperatures of the order of those used industrially for thermal decomposition of organic matter for the depths of burial to which oil-yielding rocks are believed to have been submitted. When geologically reasonable temperatures (perhaps 100° C. or decidedly less) are assigned for the formation of petroleum thermally, inordinately long times are predicted by relationships such as that of Maier and Zimmerly. The time required at 100° C., for example, is in itself not unduly long, but to this must be added the time required for a temperature of 100° C. to be attained, if that temperature is critical, or some allowance must be made for the lower rate of transformation which will obtain until burial gives a temperature of 100° C. Various factors have, however, been suggested as being capable of reducing the time required for oil generation at a given temperature. Among these are high pressures and catalysts, but it has yet to be demonstrated that these are effective under geological conditions and can lead to the required result.

Attention can now be drawn to some other problems associated with the preceding work. It is generally held that oil shales are not oil source rocks, and therefore, if this belief is correct, it would have been preferable to test the mechanism on a probable source rock. Strictly this should have been a recent source rock, because in the present state of knowledge it is not possible to be certain that a source rock which had yielded oil has not now exhausted its capacity to yield oil by whatever is the appropriate mechanism. Furthermore, it might be argued that some oil shales are sufficiently old and have been sufficiently deeply buried to have given some 'bitumen' or even oil if the thermal decomposition mechanism had been operative. This point appears not to have been investigated although it is well known.

The organic matter in oil shales or other organic deposits is complex, and experimental evidence suggests that different critical temperatures may exist below which some or other of the components do not appear to

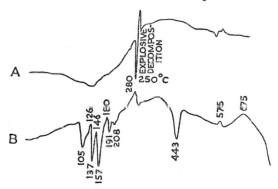

FIG. 11. Thermographic analyses of organic matter from mud off Cuba. *A*, water-insoluble fraction. *B*, water-soluble fraction. (After Whitehead and Breger.[47])

decompose. If such critical temperatures do exist, then the whole basis of extrapolation to low temperatures via relationships like that of Maier and Zimmerly breaks down; and of course it is also not in order to make experiments at temperatures other than those which obtain in Nature. The existence of different rates of break-down or of different temperature coefficients for the various reactions would create comparable problems.

In view of the above points it seems necessary to consider the rejection of much if not all of the older experimental work which has been put forward in support of the mechanism of oil formation by thermal decomposition. It is impossible to state whether or not this rejection automatically means the rejection of the mechanism itself.

Some recent experimental work by Whitehead and Breger[47] has avoided some of the criticisms set out above, although the temperature needed to give interesting results is still considerably above that which has probably obtained during oil formation in Nature. This work also affords support for the suggestion that the components in complex organic mixtures decompose at different temperatures (Fig. 11). Details are given later.

A related mechanism of oil formation, in that it also involves deep burial of the source rocks, is the hypothesis of oil formation by pressure or by shearing. Hawley[17] carried out experimental work in which organic shales were sheared in steel cylinders, but found no evidence of any increase in extractable matter due to 'bitumen' generation by shearing, as distinct from some slight increase which could be attributed to comminution of the shale making the solvent more effective. More recently Fash[12] has suggested that oil is generated by heating due to friction between mineral grains during compaction. He put forward the hypothesis that oil source rocks contained considerably less organic matter than did oil shales, and that in the latter rocks there was sufficient organic matter to act as cushions between the mineral grains, thereby preventing or reducing the generation of frictional heat. The available evidence, and in particular the experimental evidence, does not appear to afford any significant support for this hypothesis.

According to Barton[1], data which he assembled on Gulf Coast crudes indicated decreases in specific gravity and in naphthenicity with increased burial or age. He considered these phenomena to point to evolution of the crudes, and that age and depth of burial may be in some measure interchangeable. It might be argued, by extrapolating the trend of the changes backwards to less depths of burial and smaller ages, that there has been evolution from even denser and more asphaltic substances, i.e. from something nearer in composition to the parent source material; or, taking the matter a stage farther back, there has been oil formation by an agent involving depth of burial and time. On the other hand, there is no certainty that the source materials or virgin oils in the area studied were closely similar over the entire area at a given time, or at different dates in a single locality. If this original similarity did not exist, then the trends noted by Barton may not be the results of evolution of the oils; they could be due to other factors. In this connexion it may be noted that Francis[13] considers that Brooks is right when he says that 'organic materials as stable as the paraffins, once formed and sealed in the sedimentary rocks, undergo no further chemical change whatever under the conditions of temperature and pressure existing in sedimentary rocks even of great geological age and depth'. The difference in composition of younger and older oil deposits may be due more likely to differences in the source matter or in the original reactions than to a later progressive change in the oil.

Recently Haeberle[16] has studied the relationships between age, depth, and gravity (averaged) for the Gulf Coast region, and has concluded that the more marine the conditions, irrespective of age and depth, the higher the A.P.I. gravity of the oil. He suggests that the finer-grained material of the marine environment may have a catalytic action giving lighter crudes. The information is insufficient to show whether or not the more marine environment, in addition to being associated with finer-grained sediments, also had somewhat different organic matter or conditions of original formation of the crude oil. The fact that the finer-grained material was associated with the higher A.P.I. oil gravities (low densities) does not necessarily mean that the finer-grained sediments were responsible for the higher A.P.I. gravities of the crudes.

Whitehead and Breger[47] studied the effects of heating organic matter from near-shore mud obtained from shallow marine areas between the western end of Cuba and the Isle of Pines. Mangrove trees grew near the points of collection of the samples. Butyl alcohol was added to the samples as a preservative at the time of collection. The organic matter was extracted by successively treating the mud with 1:1 benzene-ethyl alcohol, ethyl alcohol, and chloroform, and the bulked extracts were evaporated to dryness at room temperature under vacuum. The resulting dark brown, malodorous solid represented 2·5 per cent. of the dried mud, and was stored under nitrogen. It included free sulphur and sodium chloride; calcium and magnesium were present, with traces of Sr, K, Ag, Ba, Ni, Cu, Fe, Cr, Mn, Ti, Si, and Al. Seventy-five per cent. of the material was water-soluble, and proved to be light brown in colour. On thermographic analysis the water-soluble material showed sharp exothermic and endothermic decomposition peaks, the lowest being at 105° C. (Fig. 11). The material insoluble in water decomposed explosively at a temperature slightly over 250° C. When the gases produced by heating the water-soluble material at 135° C. for 26 hours were analysed in a mass spectrometer, C_4, C_5, and C_6 hydrocarbons were found, and these constituted up to 20 per cent. of the gas. The hydrocarbons were indicated to be saturated, unsaturated, and cyclic. No hydrogen was produced during the pyrolysis. Hydrogen sulphide apparently was formed from the water-soluble fraction, and carbon dioxide from both fractions.

Breger and Whitehead suggest that if the water-soluble components of the mud contained catalytic agents which would be capable of assisting the conversion of the material into hydrocarbons at temperatures of 135° C. or lower, it is possible to postulate the formation of petroleum after the parent substances have migrated through rock barriers which are impermeable to hydrocarbons. Such an hypothesis, at first sight, meets some of the difficulties which have been indicated, but it is by no means certain that there would generally be that nicety of balance between the attainment of suitable temperatures, rates of fluid movement due to compaction, and the relative volumes and distribution of source, reservoir, and cap-rocks which would ensure the formation of the oil in the reservoir rocks and not in some other rock through which the compaction fluids were passing.

Radio-active transformation

The earlier studies of the occurrence of radio-active substances were concerned principally with igneous rocks and mineralized zones. However, subsequently it became clear that sedimentary rocks frequently showed considerable amounts of radio-activity (Fig. 8), and this was especially marked in the more clayey or shaly rocks. This finding could be of considerable significance since the latter rock types commonly contain more organic matter than others, and are believed to be oil source rocks in many cases. Breger and Whitehead[3] quote the case of a Miocene shale (believed to be a source rock) in California in which the radio-activity increases as the highly organic layers are approached. However, there are instances where the circumstances indicate that limestones may have been source rocks, and limestones, unless argillaceous, are low in radio-activity. This fact, of course, does not necessarily condemn the suggestion that radio-activity is the agent responsible for oil formation; it does, however, indicate that relatively feeble intensities of radio-activity may have to be considered in assessing the potentialities of this proposed mechanism.

In the course of spontaneous break-down radio-active substances emit one or more of the following: α-particles, β-particles, and γ-rays. It has long been known that these particles and rays are capable of causing the break-down of organic matter, and Lind and others have studied this type of reaction in relation to the possible formation of hydrocarbons. The laboratory work has invariably used the more powerful radio-active substances. In addition, the ratio of radio-active material to organic matter has been far higher than is the case in sediments.

According to Sheppard and Whitehead[31] the radio-activity of terrestrial materials arises principally from the uranium and thorium series, and from potassium. Potassium is the commonest of the radio-active elements. Rankama and Sahama[29] state that in argillaceous sediments (shales) the potassium content averages 2·7 per cent. K^{40}, the radio-active isotope of potassium, has a low rate of decay, and the energy of the β-particles and γ-rays it emits is small in comparison with that of the α-particles of the other two series. Hence in normal rocks the contribution of potassium to the radio-active energy is less than that of the uranium and thorium series. Mead states that when allowance is made for the presence of potassium, α-particles account for 75 per cent. of the radio-active energy produced in rocks.

Bell, Goodman, and Whitehead[2] have investigated the radio-activity of various sedimentary rocks and the associated crude oils. They considered that the radio-active content of the crude oils was quantitatively sufficient to cause appreciable cracking by α-radiation during geological time.

The radium content of a series of sandstones, shales, and limestones, ranging Ordovician to Oligocene in age, lay between 0·18 and $1·42 \times 10^{-12}$ gm./gm. of rock; the average value was $1·29 \times 10^{-12}$ gm./gm. of rock. In the crude oils the average radon content was $0·19 \times 10^{-12}$ curies/gm. and the average radium content $0·018 \times 10^{-12}$ gm./gm. The maximum and minimum values were, respectively, over twice and under one-quarter of the average. The radon:radium ratio averaged 10·5, indicating that much of the radon, a break-down product of radium, came from a source other than the radium in the oil. Measurements of the thorium were not made.

One of the points emphasized by the earlier proponents of the formation of petroleum by radio-activity was that this mechanism afforded a means of obtaining a multicomponent product from a single parent compound.[23] Briefly, the suggestion is summed up in the following chemical equation:

$$2C_nH_{2n+2} \rightleftharpoons C_{n-1}H_{2(n-1)+2} + C_{n+1}H_{2(n+1)+2}.$$

Clearly, this type of reaction would provide a complex product. Incidentally, it has also been suggested that prolonged heating of a single hydrocarbon compound could, by a comparable reaction, yield a complex product. The parent substance in the above reaction could be methane formed by bacterial decay, if the reaction holds for $n = 1$. However, hydrogen would be formed in quantity even if the starting-point was a higher member of the paraffin series, and the disposal of hydrogen is one of the problems of theoretical and experimental studies of oil formation by radio-activity. There have been suggestions that hydrogen may not be liberated in this and other reactions when the bombardment takes place under high pressure, or that it escapes by diffusion.

In the more recent experimental work on this mechanism various fatty acids have been subjected to bombardment by α-particles from radon. The main identified higher hydrocarbon produced by the bombardment has differed with the different acids used. In all cases the gaseous products have included considerable amounts of hydrogen. Carbon dioxide was frequently abundant and in some cases there were substantial amounts of carbon monoxide. Methane, ethane, and propane were usually present in small amounts.[3] Cyclohexane-carboxylic acid, which has been identified in California and Baku crudes, on bombardment by deuterons in a cyclotron yielded, along with much carbon dioxide, a liquid which was identified as cyclohexane with 12·5 per cent. of cyclohexene. A comparable result was apparently obtained by α-particle bombardment.

The bombardment of palmitic acid yielded a gas which consisted of 53·3 per cent. hydrogen, 37·8 per cent. carbon dioxide, 5·5 per cent. carbon monoxide, and 1·9 per cent. of methane, with the remainder not identified. In addition there was a small amount of liquid which, from a study of its properties, has been identified as *n*-pentadecane. Somewhat similar proportions of the various compounds were present in the gas from the bombardment of lauric acid, and in this case the liquid appeared to be *n*-undecane.

For palmitic acid the suggested mechanism is as follows:[31]

$$CH_3(CH_2)_{14}-C\diagup_{OH}^{O} \rightarrow CH_3(CH_2)_{14}-+-C\diagup_{OH}^{O}$$

$$\rightarrow CH_3(CH_2)_{14}-H+C\diagup_{O}^{O}$$

Since a variety of fatty acids and other organic materials apparently occur in the sediments (see Table XI) a complex product is possible by radio-active transformation without invoking reactions of the kind indicated by the chemical equation given on page 53.

Suggestions have been made that the hydrogen combines with unsaturated hydrocarbons to give the saturated compounds typical of petroleum. However, not only would α-particle bombardment of hydrocarbons yield hydrogen, but hydrogen, together with oxygen, would be formed by similar bombardment of water. Oxygen is not reported in uncontaminated natural gas. Thus, whether or not hydrocarbons are formed by radio-activity, there is still the problem of disposing of hydrogen and oxygen formed by the break-down of water which is to be expected when radio-active substances are present. Admittedly, if suitable bacteria were present in the sediments the oxygen could be consumed, and there are also bacteria which can utilize hydrogen. Such an explanation would call for the existence of active bacteria in the sediments long after deposition.

The production of hydrogen in the various laboratory investigations on the origin of oil through the agency of radio-activity may be a consequence of the experimental conditions, and in Nature hydrogen possibly is not one of the products.

It must also be noted that hydrogen production has been observed in various laboratory studies of bacterial action and in gases formed in lake deposits. Indeed, hydrogen formation is considered in some cases to be an intermediate stage in the production of methane.[52] If free hydrogen were to accumulate in the early phases of biochemical breakdown of organic matter, the disposal of this hydrogen would be just as much a problem as the disposal of that produced by α-particle bombardment, but in this case the presence of bacteria is not in doubt.

Proteins and other nitrogenous organic substances would yield nitrogen on bombardment, while helium would be one of the products of the break-down of certain radio-active substances. Both these elements (nitrogen and helium) are known in some natural gases, and they usually occur together. However, if radio-activity were the main agent in the transformation of organic matter to petroleum, the presence of these two elements might be expected to be a normal and fairly constant feature of natural gases. Hence, if the presence of these two elements is a rather special feature a special explanation may be warranted, and there is proximity to 'granite' basement in a number of cases.

Nitrogen has been identified in the gases developed in bottom deposits of lakes, presumably having been liberated by bacteria.

Sheppard and Whitehead[31] have applied data obtained when pentadecane was produced from palmitic acid by bombardment with α-particles, to the Antrim shale (Devonian-Carboniferous) of Michigan, and have estimated that in 1×10^7 years the oil yield by the action of α-particles would be 0·00068 gm. per gramme of sediment. It was assumed that the organic matter had 5 per cent. of free saturated fatty acids (the Chincoteague Bay material had 5 per cent. in its organic matter). Of course, some of the oil would be available long before the end of the period of 1×10^7 years, but the full time would be needed to give an amount similar to that estimated to have been formed at Santa Fe Springs, California.

Biochemical transformation

Bacteria are ubiquitous. They are found wherever there is decaying organic matter; indeed, they cause the decay. Bacteria occur in abundance in the water of seas, rivers, and lakes, and in the sediments. They have been found in sediments under great depths of water and also well below the surface of the sediments (Fig. 12). Several hundred viable bacteria per gramme (wet basis) have been found at depths of over 25 ft. in the sediments of the Gulf of California.

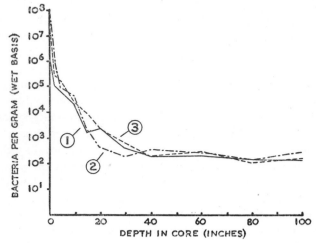

FIG. 12. Distribution of bacteria, with depth in sediment. (Based on data given by Zobell[50]).

Core	1	2	3
Location	33° 03·3′ N.; 117° 25·5′ W.	32° 36·4′ N.; 117° 27·8′ W.	32° 26·4′ N.; 117° 41·3′ W.
Depth of water	1415 ft.	3750 ft.	3120 ft.

The water content of the samples would probably be high.

Bacteria are minute organisms, a fraction of a micron to several microns in dimensions. They are capable of acting on organic compounds especially, but sometimes their activities involve inorganic substances. Generally their activities lead to the breaking down of complex organic matter to simpler substances, but there also appear to be cases of synthetic action. Bacteria are normally specific in their action, but they can at times be made to alter their tastes, and this is generally achieved by applying conditions which differ from those of their normal habitat. They and the enzymes by which they work are seriously damaged or destroyed by temperatures of 60°–100° C., depending on other conditions. The temperature coefficients of biochemical reactions are fairly high, and in addition bacteria and enzymes have a temperature of optimum activity which is not independent of the time factor considered. Since biochemical decompositions of complex substances are usually a chain of reactions, at temperatures removed from that which gives a maximum yield of a given end-product in a set time, other (intermediate) products may become apparent and accumulate, owing to the succeeding reactions not being able to utilize them as quickly as they are formed. Laboratory incubations are often carried out at 30° C., which is appreciably higher than the temperatures under which some biochemical reactions may begin in Nature.

In trying to obtain hydrocarbons by biochemical processes in the laboratory, it must be remembered that bacterial forms and activities may vary under different physical and chemical conditions. Fermentation may not take place, or may follow a different course, when using relatively pure materials. Some of the bacterial forms produced may be abnormal and incapable of reproduction, whilst others may persist only so long as the special conditions obtain, and may develop properties which are latent, absent, or masked in the original strain. It is not impossible that under moderately high pressures micro-organisms may form rather different compounds from a given substrate from those produced under atmospheric pressure, since pressure aids the polymerization of unsaturated substances in particular.

There is evidence that the constitution of the surface of bacteria is not uniform, and it is likely that many of the reactions in which they are involved take place outside the organisms.

Two main groups of bacteria are recognized according as their activities are dependent on or independent of the presence of free oxygen in the environment in which they occur. These are referred to as aerobes and anaerobes, respectively. Anaerobes satisfy their oxygen requirements by breaking down oxygen-containing compounds. Consequently the products formed by bacteria in an anaerobic environment tend to be comparatively low in oxygen, whereas those formed in an aerobic environment contain an abundance of that element in combined form. Broadly the aerobic decompositions generally involve more extensive breakdown of the organic substances than do anaerobic decompositions. Examination of the differences in bulk composition of organic matter and petroleum shows that the oxygen content is relatively low in the latter, a condition which may be expected if petroleum is formed by bacterial decomposition of organic matter under anaerobic conditions. It has previously been noted that the environments which appear to be favourable for the formation of oil source rocks would be likely to include among their characteristics a deficiency in free oxygen. This feature can be due in part to the activities of bacteria, and has been extensively discussed by Zobell.[48]

Another chemical factor which can affect the activities of bacteria is the pH of the medium, and as with the state of reduction mentioned above, this factor also can be modified by bacterial activities. Indeed, it is well known that bacteria may produce acid products which, if they are allowed to accumulate, may finally inhibit further bacterial action. Zobell has suggested that conditions inimical to the activity of hydro-carbon-oxidizing micro-organisms appear to be necessary for the accu-mulation of petroleum in recent sediments.[49] It has been reported that many samples of petroleum and oil-well brines have bacteriostatic prop-erties, although the exact cause of these properties is not known. Experiments have shown that certain heavy metals (small amounts of zinc, vanadium, or molybdenum), the presence of hydrogen sulphide, low redox potentials (measures of the state of oxidation or reduction of a system), and specific oxidase inhibitors prevent the microbial oxi-dation of hydrocarbons. It is worthy of note that not only do some aerobic bacteria destroy hydrocarbons, but certain species of sulphate-reducers also can assimilate the higher aliphatic hydrocarbons. Sulphate-reducing bacteria have been found in abundance in nearly all samples of recent marine sediments investigated, and they have also been reported in oilfield waters. In the latter case it is debatable as to whether the bacteria are indigenous to the formations, or have been introduced during drilling. However, certain features such as the pre-sence of peculiar types of organism, the ability of the organisms to function under conditions equivalent to those of the oil reservoir, and their continued presence after long periods of production suggest that they are indigenous. Nevertheless, these bacteria are not neces-sarily the descendants of those entombed at the time of formation of the sediments; conditions can be visualized under which a more recent entry (although not during drilling) is possible in some cases. The low sulphate content of oilfield waters and the reduced sulphate content of waters at a small depth in recent sediments point to the activity of sulphate-reducers.

Organic matter, whether animal or vegetable, is a protein-carbo-hydrate-fat complex often containing unsaturated compounds, whereas petroleum is dominantly hydrocarbon, saturated, and with relatively small amounts of combined sulphur, nitrogen, and oxygen.

Table XIV gives data on the average composition of fats, proteins, and carbohydrates, and it is evident from the point of view of the pro-portions of the different elements that the fats would require least modification to be equivalent to petroleum, while the proteins would be next in this respect.

TABLE XIV

(After C. G. Rogers)

Element	Average composition of organic matter		
	Fats	Proteins	Carbohydrates
	%	%	%
Oxygen . .	17·90	22·4	49·88
Carbon . .	69·05	51·3	44·44
Hydrogen .	10·00	6·9	6·18
Phosphorus	2·13	0·7	..
Nitrogen .	0·61	17·8	..
Sulphur .	0·31	0·8	..
Iron . .	..	0·1	..

A number of years ago the results of laboratory investigations of the action of bacteria on the various main types of organic compounds were reviewed.[18] In work on fats, proteins, carbohydrates, &c., methane was the only hydrocarbon formed in quantity, although there were occasional suggestions of the formation of small amounts of higher hydrocarbons (e.g. see Table VII). Substantial amounts of hydrogen, sulphuretted hydrogen, and carbon dioxide were reported in many instances. The last two gases are well-known components of numerous natural gases, but hydrogen, if present at all, occurs only in traces. Various suggestions can be offered to try to explain the failure to obtain hydrocarbons other than methane, and these can be summed up in the observation that the laboratory studies did not closely approach the conditions under which the organic matter in sediments might be converted biochemically to petroleum. Consequently the results of these laboratory studies may not be conclusive in relation to this problem. Briefly, the natural conditions would probably involve the following: (a) a complicated mixture of organic substances, with some of those which are not easily broken down possibly prominent; (b) a temperature which was not much above the sea temperature; (c) a pressure above atmospheric, but perhaps only a few atmospheres above; (d) finely divided organic matter, intimately mixed with mineral matter and, most commonly, with saline water; (e) absence of light; (f) a micro-flora in substantial equilibrium with its environment, i.e. groupings of species and individuals which gave a balanced or only slowly changing population; and (g) little or no free oxygen.

There had been vague reports of the formation in fermentations of 'gaseous paraffins' and of unsaturated hydrocarbons. More recently Zobell has reported the experimental biochemical production of 34 mgm. of ether-soluble, unsaponifiable, oil-like material from 1·2 gm. of caproic acid, and this oil-like material was indicated by tests to consist largely of normal paraffins ranging from $C_{20}H_{42}$ to $C_{25}H_{52}$. Comparable experiments have yielded small amounts of oil-like extracts from acetic, propionic, butyric, capric, stearic, and lactic acids.

It has also been stated that balkashite, a liquid, petroleum-like hydrocarbon complex, is formed anaerobically by bacteria from fats and palmitic acid.

Sisler and Zobell[32] have reported that 0·72 gm. of CCl_4-soluble material was extracted from the bacterial cell substance developed in a mineral salt medium by cultures of a species of *Desulfovibrio*. The organisms consumed hydrogen and reduced sulphate almost completely to H_2S, in addition to removing CO_2 (as carbonate, bicarbonate, and CO_2). The CCl_4 extract contained 0·21 gm. of oily unsaponifiable matter consisting largely of combined hydrogen and carbon. Infra-red spectra of this unsaponifiable matter furnished partial, but not complete, evidence that the compounds present were composed mainly of saturated —CH_2— groups with possibly some C—CH_3 groups. There was no evidence of other groups, and therefore it was concluded that the compounds present were probably paraffinic or naphthenic hydrocarbons. The sample was insufficiently large to establish that there could not be very small amounts of compounds with C—O, C=O, or O—H linkages.

TABLE XV

Results of growing of a sulphate-reducer for 45 days at 32° C. in 16 litres of a mineral salts solution overlain by H_2

Total amount of H_2 consumed	19,500 ml.
Total amount of CO_2 consumed (including carbonates) . . .	4,110 „
Total amount of H_2S produced	2,155 „
Weight of cell substance recovered (dry basis)	3·67 gm.
Weight of CCl_4-soluble fraction (amber-coloured grease) . .	0·75 „
Weight of unsaponifiable material	0·148 „

These same organisms were also able to use CO_2 as the sole hydrogen acceptor when grown in mineral salts solutions containing less than one part per million of sulphate (impurity in reagents). The growth was less rapid than in similar media enriched with sulphate.

As noted earlier, bacteria have been shown to produce hydrogen and carbon dioxide from organic compounds. Presumably these two gases might be consumed by bacteria of the types used by Sisler and Zobell, with the production of hydrocarbons in the cell substance. If this is a stage in the formation of petroleum, an explanation must be offered for the complete or almost complete disappearance of hydrogen on all occasions, while variable amounts of carbon dioxide remain.

It is a matter of speculation as to the extent to which the material recovered by Smith from the off-shore cores consisted of bacterial cell substance. Such substances would satisfy the condition of similar age to the enclosing sediment. Smith[34] reports that hydrocarbons from several sections of the Grande Isle core gave ages of 11,800–14,600± 1,400 years by C^{14} analyses, while a composite carbonate sample from the entire core gave 12,300±1,200 years. Smith also notes that extracts from barnacles reveal the presence of polynuclear aromatic compounds, while oysters and blue-fish have 45–58 p.p.m. (dry weight) of hydrocarbons. Thus the hydrocarbons detected in the cores may have come from several sources.

Catalysts

From time to time there have been suggestions that catalysts cause organic matter to be transformed to petroleum in Nature at temperatures substantially lower for a given rate of reaction than those used experimentally in studying thermal conversion. In recent years the employment of catalysts to facilitate certain reactions in the refining and cracking of petroleum has brought these suggestions to the fore again, and, in particular, emphasis has been laid on clay minerals in this connexion.[7] At present this mechanism is not proved for the formation of crude oils, and it is necessary to draw attention to the conditions obtaining in the refinery processes. The minerals employed in the catalytic processes are dry, whereas in Nature the clays or other minerals will be intimately mixed with water. The presence of water may make a profound difference to the ability of the clays to catalyse hydrocarbon reactions, and until there is experimental evidence employing more natural conditions the suggestions involving clays must be treated with reserve.

In a recent article[8] on this hypothesis of catalytic action Brooks wrote that it is necessary to assume the unprovable postulate that in their natural moist state the acid silicates have sufficient catalytic activity at low temperatures to carry on certain reactions slowly but effectively over a period of millions of years. The rate of transformation suggested by this statement is not clearly defined, but may be inferred to be low.

There have also been suggestions that enzymes produced bacterially may be able to effect certain transformations on organic matter in the sediments, even after the death of the bacteria. These enzymes may be soluble in water or oil, and hence may be more favourably placed for catalysis than the clay minerals. It also appears that the enzymes may be active at temperatures similar to those which are favourable for bacterial activity. Because of this, and their derivation from bacteria, it seems that if enzymes are effective in this connexion the reactions can broadly be considered to fall within the sphere of the hypothesis of biochemical oil formation.

Some statistical considerations

In tackling an extremely difficult problem such as that of the origin of oil, it is necessary to try many different lines of approach. Associations must be sought and, where they exist, carefully examined for their significance. Some associations may be in the relationship of cause and effect, whereas others may not be interdependent, but the consequence of some common condition. From the point of view of aiding in the ultimate solving of these problems, within limits it may be almost as important to report negative as well as positive results.

Fig. 13 shows data on the average organic carbon contents of certain formations and areas in U.S.A (from Trask and Patnode's tabulations[10]), as well as the ratios of the indicated producible oil reserves in rocks of the same periods and the lengths of those periods (derived from Table VI). Trask and Patnode's 32,000 well samples were obtained from 164 oilfields or areas. In some fields a number of wells were used, and as many as 200 samples were obtained from a single well. Not all the U.S.A. petroliferous areas were sampled, and very extensive areas of U.S.A. were not covered. The general areas in which the wells lay comprise those responsible for the bulk of the U.S.A. reserves and past production. Statistical studies of these data have yielded a correlation coefficient of 0·64 between the ratio oil reserves of system/length (time) of system and the average (not weighted) organic carbon content of the rocks of the corresponding periods. The value of the correlation coefficient is statistically significant, and could be taken to indicate some relationship between the two quantities, namely, the higher the organic carbon content the greater the amount of oil. This implication needs to be considered in conjunction with the remarks about the possible nature and significance of the reported organic contents of ancient sediments (see pp. 40, 41). Moreover, the limitations of the basic data must be recognized. It is difficult to decide how far the organic carbon contents used are representative of the rocks of the various periods, and there is no proof that the indicated ultimate oil recoveries (production plus estimated reserves) are necessarily proportional to the eventual oil recoveries (and to the oil in place). Oil has undoubtedly been lost from former accumulations, and, broadly, the older the rocks the more likely is such loss to have taken place. Furthermore, oil may have migrated

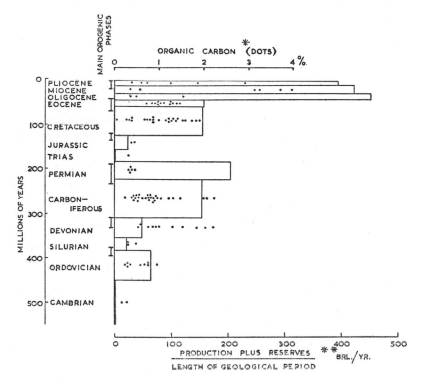

FIG. 13.

* Data from Trask and Patnode.[40]

** Data from Table VI. The areas of the rectangles are proportional to the quantity of producible oil estimated for each period. All the information is for U.S.A. The main orogenic phases are shown by vertical lines with short cross lines at the ends.

from one system to another. Nevertheless, the odds are over twenty to one against the above correlation coefficient being the consequence of chance.

The validity of the use of the factor oil reserves of system/length (time) of system is debatable, but it does seem necessary to employ a quantity which may average the oil over the system if a relation with average organic content is sought. However, mean sedimentation rates may have differed in the different systems, and some allowance for the mass of rock embracing the oil reserves and samples for organic carbon would have been preferable.

An assessment and some further points

In the preceding pages some of the main features associated with three possible means of oil formation have been briefly described. In addition, what appear to be the principal conditions which must be satisfied for oil formation in Nature and likely types of source material have been indicated. The available data clearly do not permit the mechanism of oil formation to be set out in detail, but there seem to be certain pointers favouring the predominant action of bacteria. First, bacteria are certainly present in what are considered to be the environments in which source rocks are believed to be formed. They can be active under anaerobic conditions. Secondly, the conditions of temperature and pressure to which source and reservoir rocks have been subjected are such as would have permitted the action of bacteria. Admittedly the laboratory work on the biochemical formation of petroleum has provided little more than slight suggestions of the feasibility of this mechanism; on the other hand, to date the formation of petroleum-like substances thermally has been achieved only by the use of temperatures which are not geologically acceptable. These substances differ considerably from crude oil. Bacteria could start the process of oil formation early in the history of the source sediments, with the prospect that oil would be available to move towards reservoir rocks before the permeability of the source rocks, if shales or clays, was reduced to a very low value.

That radio-activity may have caused some break-down of organic matter in the sediments, or some changes in hydrocarbons developed in the sediments by means other than radio-activity, cannot at present be denied. Indeed, it must be recognized as a definite possibility, with the main argument restricted to the extent of operation of this agent rather than to its capacity to cause changes under geologically acceptable conditions.

So far as current knowledge goes, time and temperature considerations jointly provide the main objections to the acceptance of the thermal transformation mechanism. Indeed, it appears that these considerations must provide the main basis for selecting a preferred mechanism until there is more direct evidence, and if the correct deductions have been drawn from circumstantial evidence.

Anaerobic conditions would seem to be no bar to the action of heat or radio-activity, but rather an aid in ensuring, as for bacteria, the presence of organic matter for conversion to oil and gas.

There is the possibility that the oil being formed might vary in composition with time. Consequently, that migrating early might differ from that leaving the source rock later. Whether passage into a single reservoir would lead to a homogeneous oil or whether, due to incomplete mixing, some of the differences would be preserved, is not known, but it is worthy of note that there are seemingly well-authenticated cases of variation of oil gravity with depth in a single accumulation.[11] It should be noted that there have been suggestions that these variations are due to some measure of gravitational separation, but other possible explanations merit consideration.

It seems likely that some carbon dioxide and hydrogen sulphide would be formed in the process of transforming organic matter to petroleum biochemically. Both these compounds are quite soluble in water, and in certain concentrations could inhibit further activity by some types of bacteria at least. The onward passage of water from a reservoir, while the hydrocarbons were retained, would mean that some of these two compounds could escape in solution from the reservoir rock. This escape might postpone the attainment of inhibitory concentrations of these gases. The position in the source rock might be similar if water is passing by compaction from a non-oil-forming zone into an oil-forming zone. When flow ceases or is greatly reduced, any continued bacterial formation of these or other toxic products might eventually cause a cessation of the bacterial activity. On the other hand, exhaustion of the compounds, organic or inorganic, required for the biochemical production of carbon dioxide or hydrogen sulphide would obviously terminate this form of bacterial activity. These two products might react with inorganic components of the sediments, and the former, by aiding the solution of calcium carbonate, could lead to porosity changes in rocks containing this substance. However, the question of the solubility of calcium carbonate is complex, and the preceding suggestion may be true only under a limited range of physical and chemical conditions.

The production of carbon dioxide would be far greater in an aerobic environment than in an anaerobic environment for a given supply of organic matter in the sediments. In the former case oxygen to give carbon dioxide may be obtained from sulphates, combined oxygen in the organic matter, and dissolved oxygen in the water; in the latter case the first two sources alone are available. Hence solution of calcium carbonate may be much more marked in sediments in an aerobic environment, as noted by Weeks, than in an anaerobic environment.

The reactions leading to the production of carbon dioxide and hydrogen sulphide may be in part, at least, associated with hydrocarbon destruction. It is also probable, other things being equal, that in this case they will proceed most vigorously when the oil-water interfacial area is large, i.e. before the oil is aggregated into a more or less continuous mass. Thus the mere process of accumulation will in itself tend to reduce the rate of hydrocarbon destruction by bacteria. It may therefore be argued that under what might be described as closed conditions the activities of hydrocarbon-destroying bacteria should diminish, even if they do not cease completely. However, should erosion or faulting permit the entry of water bearing suitable nutrients, hydrocarbon destruction could once more become appreciable.

REFERENCES

1. BARTON, D. C., *Problems of Petroleum Geology*, 109–55, Amer. Assoc. Petrol. Geol., 1934.
2. BELL, K. G., GOODMAN, C., and WHITEHEAD, W. L., *Bull. Amer. Assoc. Petrol. Geol.*, **24**, 1529–47 (1940).
3. BREGER, I. A., and WHITEHEAD, W. L., *Third World Petroleum Congress, The Hague, 1951*, 421–6.
4. BRONGERSMA-SANDERS, M., ibid., 401–13.
5. BROOKS, B. T., *J. Inst. Pet. Tech.*, **20**, 177–90 (1934).
6. —— *Bull. Amer. Assoc. Petrol. Geol.*, **20**, 280–300 (1936).
7. —— ibid., **32**, 2269–86 (1948).
8. —— *Ind. Eng. Chem.*, **44**, 2570–7 (Nov. 1952).
9. COX, B. B., *Bull. Amer. Assoc. Petrol. Geol.*, **30**, 645–59 (1945).
10. EMMONS, W. H., *Geology of Petroleum*, 80–93, McGraw-Hill Book Co. Inc., 1921.
11. ESPACH, R. H., and FRY, J. J., *Petrol. Tech.*, **3** (3), A.I.M.M.E. Tech. Paper No. 3018, 75–82 (1951).
12. FASH, R. H., *Bull. Amer. Assoc. Petrol. Geol.*, **28**, 1510–18 (1944).
13. FRANCIS, A. W., *The Science of Petroleum*, iii, 2098, Oxford University Press, 1938.
14. GRAHAM, J. I., and SHAW, A., *Trans. Inst. Min. Eng.*, **73**, 529–37 (1927).
15. GRAY, T., ibid., **39**, 206 (1909–10).
16. HAEBERLE, F. R., *Bull. Amer. Assoc. Petrol. Geol.*, **35**, 2238–48 (1951).
17. HAWLEY, H. E., ibid., **13**, 303–28 (1929).
18. HOBSON, G. D., *The Science of Petroleum*, i, 54–56, Oxford University Press, 1938.
19. HOFER, H. VON, *Trans. A.I.M.E.*, **48**, 481 (1914).
20. HOLMES, A., *Trans. Geol. Soc. Glasgow*, **21** (1), 117–52 (1945–6).
21. HOPKINS, G. R., *J. Petrol. Tech.*, **2**, 6–9 (June 1950).
22. ILLING, V. C., *The Science of Petroleum*, i, 32–38, Oxford University Press, 1938.
23. LIND, S. C., ibid., 39–41, Oxford University Press, 1938.
24. LOVELY, H. R., *Bull. Amer. Assoc. Petrol. Geol.*, **30**, 1444–516 (1946).
25. MAIER, C. G., and ZIMMERLY, S. R., *Bull. Univ. Utah*, **14** (7), 62–81.
26. MCNAB, J. G., SMITH, P. V., and BETTS, R. L., *Ind. Eng. Chem.*, **44**, 2556–63 (Nov. 1952).

27. NEUMANN, L. M., BASS, N. W., GINTER, R. L., MAUNEY, S. F., RYNIKER, C., and SMITH, H. M., *Bull. Amer. Assoc. Petrol. Geol.*, **25**, 1801–9 (1941).
28. RANKAMA, K., *J. Geol.*, **56**, 199–209 (1948).
29. RANKAMA, K., and SAHAMA, Th. G., *Geochemistry*, 432, University of Chicago Press, 1950.
30. RAWN, A. M., BANTA, A. P., and POMEROY, R., *Trans. Amer. Soc. Civ. Eng.*, **104**, 93–99 (1939).
31. SHEPPARD, C. W., and WHITEHEAD, W. L., *Bull. Amer. Assoc. Petrol. Geol.*, **30**, 32–51 (1946).
32. SISLER, F. D., and ZOBELL, C. E., *J. Bact.*, **62**, 121 (1951).
33. SMITH, P. V., *Bull. Amer. Assoc. Petrol. Geol.*, **36**, 411–13 (1952).
34. —— *Science*, **116**, 437–9 (1952).
35. SPICER, H. C., *Handbook of Physical Constants*, Geol. Soc. Amer., Special Paper No. 36 (1942).
36. STEBINGER, E., *World Geography of Petroleum*, edited by W. E. Pratt and D. Good, Princeton University Press, 1950.
37. TRASK, P. D., *Origin and Environment of Source Beds of Petroleum*, Gulf Publishing Co., 1932.
38. —— *Bull. Amer. Assoc. Petrol. Geol.*, **20**, 245–7 (1936).
39. —— *Recent Marine Sediments*, 442, 443, 445, Amer. Assoc. Petrol. Geol., 1939.
40. TRASK, P. D., and PATNODE, H. W., *Source Beds of Petroleum*, Amer. Assoc. Petrol. Geol., 1942.
41. TRASK, P. D., and WU, C. C., *Bull. Amer. Assoc. Petrol. Geol.*, **14**, 1455–63 (1930).
42. TWENHOFEL, W. H., and McELVEY, V. E., ibid., **25**, 826–9 (1941).
43. —— —— *J. Sed. Pet.*, **12**, 36–50 (1942).
44. WARREN, C. M., and STORER, F. H., *Acad. Arts and Sci. Mem.*, 2nd series, **9**, 177.
45. WEEKS, L. G., *Bull. Amer. Assoc. Petrol. Geol.*, **36**, 2071–124 (1952).
46. WELLS, R. C., and ERICKSON, E. T., *U.S.G.S. Prof. Paper No. 186*, 69–79.
47. WHITEHEAD, W. L., and BREGER, I. A., *Science*, **111**, 335–7 (1950).
48. ZOBELL, C. E., *Bull. Amer. Assoc. Petrol. Geol.*, **30**, 477–513 (1946).
49. —— *Bact. Reviews*, **10**, 1–49 (1946).
50. —— *Marine Microbiology*, 94, Chronica Botanica Co., 1946.
51. —— *Fundamental Research on Occurrence and Recovery of Petroleum*, 105–13, A.P.I., 1943.
52. —— *Science*, **102**, 364–9 (1945).
53. —— *Third World Petroleum Congress, The Hague, 1951*, 414–20.
54. ZOBELL, C. E., GRANT, C. W., and HAAS, H. F., *Bull. Amer. Assoc. Petrol. Geol.*, **27**, 1175–93 (1943).

IV

MIGRATION AND ACCUMULATION

A NUMBER of features support the belief that a phase of migration is an essential part of the process of forming an oil or gas accumulation. These include the following: (*a*) the arrangement of the gas, oil, and water in the order of their densities; (*b*) the occurrence of the oil and gas in what is locally the highest accessible part of the reservoir rock; (*c*) the concentration of newly formed oil or gas in the source rock is thought to be quite low, and even the most ardent believer in high concentrations of source material as being essential would not grant concentrations which would yield oil and gas *in situ* to occupy the greater part of the pores in which they are now found; and (*d*) many reservoir rocks are considered to be impossible or improbable oil source rocks. These features form a sound basis for believing that oil and gas migration takes place not only within the reservoir rock but also, in many instances, from a separate source rock into the reservoir rock. The density arrangement, structural position, and concentration are most unlikely to be original.

Any discussion of oil migration should start with knowledge or assumptions regarding (*a*) the condition of the hydrocarbons, and (*b*) their environment at the time migration takes place. Thus views on oil origin are involved, and unless the above points are covered clearly the scene is only vaguely set for the presentation of a mechanism of oil and gas migration. The salient points about oil origin which will be assumed as a basis for the ensuing discussion of migration are as follows: (1) oil and gas are generally formed in fine-grained sediments; (2) the oil and gas exist in these sediments as discrete liquid and gaseous globules; (3) the liquid and gaseous hydrocarbon content of the source rock is but a small proportion of the total fluid content at the time of formation; and (4) the oil and gas are formed geologically early in the history of the sediment, i.e. before the sediment is extensively compacted.

The two phases of migration involved in the formation of an oil accumulation, when the source and reservoir rocks differ, are (*a*) the transfer of oil and gas from the source to the reservoir rock (primary migration), and (*b*) the segregation of oil and gas within the reservoir rock and their emplacement in the highest available position (secondary migration).

The values of the density, viscosity, interfacial tension, and other properties of crude oils at the time of migration are not known with certainty. In the absence of this knowledge it is necessary to assume that the values measured on crudes as they are now (discussed in Chapter II) are a fair guide to the values of the same properties at the time of migration. Some allowance can be made for the influence of changes of physical conditions on the values of these properties, but no accurate allowance can be made for the effects of any evolution of the crude which may have taken place subsequent to or during migration. It has been suggested that this evolution may be in the direction of decreasing density with increased age and/or depth of burial. Qualitative allowance could be made for such an effect. The wide ranges of the current values for the various physical properties of the crudes might mean that some crudes had properties within these ranges at the time of migration, but this might not be true for others. A further difficulty arises in the absence of clear knowledge of the time which elapses between the formation of oil and its migration. The possibility of a recurrence of secondary migration or of adjustments is freely admitted, and some geologists suggest the possibility of successive phases of primary migration. All these uncertainties put severe restrictions on attempts to examine some phenomena quantitatively. Nevertheless, this quantitative approach must be made wherever possible in order to obtain guidance on the relative merits of different hypotheses.

The data presented in Chapter II show that the range of variation of oil densities is relatively small, but since the effective quantity in some phenomena under subsurface conditions will be the difference between the water density and the oil density, the range of relative values of this quantity may be quite large. The range of the values of oil viscosities is large, but there is uncertainty about the effective values under the conditions obtaining early in the history of an oil accumulation. The range of interfacial tension values at the time of oil migration may be comparable with that now observed. It should be noted that the density and interfacial tension may largely determine the forces available for causing certain fluid movements, while viscosity will partially control the rate of movement.

Some fundamental concepts

When a globule of one fluid exists within a second fluid there is a pressure difference across the interface between the two fluids. This is such as to cause the pressure within the globule to be greater than in the surrounding fluid. For a spherical globule of radius r cm., the excess pressure will be p dynes/cm². , where $p = 2T/r$, and T dynes/cm. is the interfacial tension between the two fluids. Pressure differences may obtain across any curved fluid interface, and these will be dependent on the curvature, as in the above relationship; the condition is not restricted to globules which are approximately spherical in form.

The relationship shows that the excess pressure is greater the smaller the radius of curvature. Hence, if a globule is distorted and thereby the radius of curvature is decreased, the pressure within it will be increased,

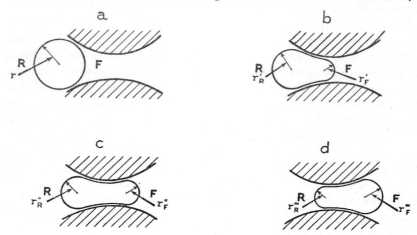

Fig. 14. Stages in the passage of a globule through a throat. The ruled areas are parts of mineral grains, and the globule is separated from these grains by an immiscible fluid.

i.e. work will have been done on the globule. In this process the surface area of the globule increases, and the change in surface area is an alternative means of assessing the work done on the globule.

Pores in rocks are not of constant cross-section, but show expansions and contractions (throats). A globule which is of greater diameter than the diameter of a throat cannot pass through that throat without undergoing deformation to a shape with greater curvature. This implies that work must be done to cause the globule to pass through such a throat. The process is shown diagrammatically in Figs. 14 *a–d*. In Fig. 14 *a* an undeformed globule of radius r is shown. In Fig. 14 *b* the globule has been forced into the throat. The curvature $1/r'_F$ at the fore end is greater than at the rear end, i.e. $r^R > r'_F$. Consequently the pressure differential across the fore end is greater than across the rear end. However, the internal pressure must be constant at any level within the globule when it is not in motion, and the globule can be retained in the position shown only by an applied external pressure which is greater at the rear end than at the fore end.

In Fig. 14 c the fore end of the globule has passed beyond the narrowest part of the throat, and $r_F'' > r_F'$, while $r_R'' < r_R'$. Since $r_R'' > r_F''$ a larger external pressure is still necessary at the rear than at the fore end to keep the globule in position. In Fig. 14 d the globule has advanced farther so that $r_F''' > r'''$. The pressure differential across the meniscus will now be less at F than at R, and the globule can be kept in this position only by applying a suitable greater external pressure at the fore end than at the rear end. If this balancing pressure is not applied the globule will advance spontaneously, the rear end being drawn through the throat.

The entire process of passage of a globule through a throat is thus characterized by a phase of relatively slow penetration and partial passage until the fore end is less curved than the rear end, after which interfacial forces, which previously have resisted movement, assist movement progressively until the globule (or the fore end of a complex globule) has attained a maximum radius (minimum curvature) conformable with the pore geometry, the external pressures, and its own mass. As a consequence of these different stages of movement, globules being driven forward advance jerkily or spasmodically.

A pore will generally have more than two throats providing connexions with adjacent pores. These throats may differ in size, just as pores in normal rocks will differ in size, and they will have different orientations. A globule will enter or leave a pore by the throat which involves the least expenditure of energy. Throat size and orientation will therefore play some part in this choice.

Craze[2] has obtained casts in Wood's metal showing the probable form of residual oil in sandstone and limestone. Molten metal was used to displace water from water-saturated rock, and then the rock was flushed with hot water to carry out some of the metal. On cooling the metal remaining within the rock solidified, and was extracted by removal of the mineral matter. These casts (Fig. 15) show the general features inherent in the schematic representation of an oil stringer in Fig. 16. Complicated branching of a globule is undoubtedly a common condition. It is possible that some of the distortions to which a stringer may be subjected in the course of advancing will cause instability in a waist and the breaking off of a section. On the other hand, stringers may coalesce when a lobe enters a pore already containing a lobe of another stringer.

If the fluid of the complex globule or stringer (Fig. 16) is stationary and there is no flow of the surrounding fluid, the curvatures at A and D, assumed to be at the same level, will be identical, but those at B and C will be different from that at A and D, because B is higher and C lower

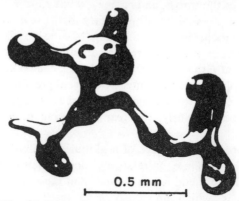

FIG. 15. Form of residual mass of Wood's metal after displacing the molten metal from sandstone (after Craze[2]).

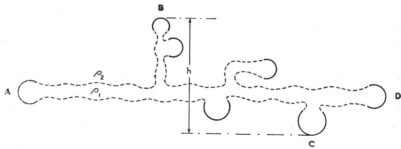

FIG. 16. Hypothetical form of stringer of oil or gas in a water-wet sandstone.

than A or D. In all cases the curvature considered is the free curvature in the pores.

Suppose that B is h cm. above C, and that the fluid in the globule is of density ρ_1, while the density of the surrounding fluid is ρ_2. Let the pressure at level C in the external fluid be P dynes/cm². Then at level B the pressure in the same fluid will be $P - h\rho_2 g$. If meniscus C is of radius r_C, the pressure in the globule fluid at level C will be $P + 2T/r_C$. At level B in the globule fluid the pressure will therefore be $P + 2T/r_C - h\rho_1 g$. If meniscus B is of radius r_B, the pressure differential across this meniscus will be $2T/r_B$, whence the pressure in the external fluid will be $P + 2T/r_C - h\rho_1 g - 2T/r_B$, which has previously been shown to be

$P-h\rho_2 g$. Thus $2T/r_C-h\rho_1 g-2T/r_B = -h\rho_2 g$, which, on rearrangement, gives $2T (1/r_C-1r_B) = gh(\rho_1-\rho_2)$. If $\rho_1 > \rho_2$, $1/r_C$ will be greater than $1/r_B$, i.e. r_B will be greater than r_C; if $\rho_1 < \rho_2$, r_C will be greater than r_B. The latter condition will obtain when oil or gas globules occur in water, or gas globules in oil, the oil having a density less than that of water.

For a given system T, ρ_1 and ρ_2 will be fixed, and hence variations in the value of h will cause variations in the relative values of r_C and r_B, without fixing the absolute value of either of these quantities. It will be apparent that if by accretion h is increased the radii at B and C, as controlled by globule mass and pore geometry, may become such that B may pass through a throat pointing upwards or sideways while the meniscus C retracts upwards slightly. In this way an oil mass greater than a critical height, determined by the interfacial tension, density, and pore and throat sizes, may rise through the pores of a rock by virtue of buoyancy in water, or a gas mass may rise in oil.

It can readily be shown that for geometrically similar packings of uniform spherical grains the critical height needed to give buoyant rise of an oil or gas mass is inversely proportional to the radius of the grains.

In tight packing of uniform spherical grains[3] of diameter D the larger pore can accommodate a sphere of diameter $0{\cdot}414$ D, and the smaller pore one of diameter $0{\cdot}22$ D, while the throats will permit the passage of a sphere of diameter $0{\cdot}154$ D. If the diameter of the grains is $0{\cdot}5$ mm., the oil density $0{\cdot}85$ gm./c.c., and the interfacial tension between the oil and water 20 dynes/cm., the maximum critical height for buoyant rise will be about 44 cm.; an intermediate critical height involving the smaller pore will be about 22 cm.

Simple experiments have provided evidence supporting the view that, other things being equal, the finer the rock the greater the critical height necessary for the oil or gas mass to move upwards under the sole influence of buoyancy. Sand was sedimented in water in glass tubes with their axes vertical. Oil was introduced at the top end, and the length of general infilling with oil (by partial displacement of the water) was apparent, because the oil could be seen through the glass. When a suitable length was filled the inlet and outlet were closed and the tubes inverted. Careful observation showed that for a given sand and oil, after some time signs of oil appeared appreciably above the zone of known infilling, when the infilling exceeded a critical height. This critical height was greater the finer the sand.

Suppose that water is caused to flow horizontally past the stringer shown in Fig. 16 and that the pressure gradient in this external fluid is α dynes/cm.²/cm. This flow will cause adjustments in the form of the stringer as compared with the form when no flow was taking place. Let the pressure in the water at A be P; then at D, which is l cm. from A, the pressure in the water will be $P-\alpha l$. For stability the pressure inside the stringer at A must be equal to that inside at D. Thus the curvature at A must be less than at D, because that gives a smaller pressure differential across the meniscus at A than at D, thereby offsetting the higher external pressure at A than at D. For a stringer of given mass in a porous medium the flowing water will cause a process of adjustment which will increase the curvature at D, and will simultaneously alter the curvature at A and elsewhere in the stringer. Some advance will be associated with this adjustment, in an attempt to obtain stable equilibrium.

Ultimately D may become sufficiently curved to pass through a throat, and subsequently the curvature at D will decrease. The internal pressure difference between A and D will then diminish, and at a certain point some spontaneous movement of the stringer will occur. In some respects the advance of the stringer under the influence of the pressure gradient in the surrounding liquid is due to a process resembling squeezing. l fixes the critical difference in the pressure differentials in relation to throat and pore sizes, coupled with stringer mass. It will be apparent that at any time the part of a complex globule which is penetrating and passing through a throat may not necessarily be at the leading end of the globule; it may be at some intermediate point at which the critical conditions have been passed. Other things being equal, long stringers may be in motion while shorter stringers are stationary.

In a porous medium with throats of constant size, globules of density less than that of the surrounding fluid will rise gradually as they advance under the influence of the horizontally flowing external fluid, because buoyancy will give a slight bias in favour of penetration of upward-directed throats. This tendency will exist also where there are differences in throat size which are not offset by the other factors, such as small density differences or too small vertical dimensions of the oil mass.

The natural rate of water movement through an aquifer undoubtedly varies widely, and Meinzer and Wenzel[11] have indicated a range of 5ft./day to 5 ft./year. A possible average rate is given as 50 ft./year. If the porosity is 20 per cent. and the permeability of the rock 100 mD, with the temperature 40° C., the pressure gradient for this rate of flow will be about 64 dynes/cm.²/cm. Gradients of this order causing water flow in uniform tight-packed sands with grains of 0·05 cm. diameter would mean that the maximum critical stringer length would be 1 m.

Some discussions of oil and gas movement in areas such as the Rocky Mountain states of U.S.A. have involved artesian circulation. For such cases the water velocities noted above may be relevant, but rates of movement in highly permeable beds included in a compacting series and transmitting water expressed by compaction are much more speculative, although estimates might be possible for specified conditions.

The hydraulic gradients for horizontal carriage of oil or gas by water will be greater than for upward carriage and less than for downward carriage. The figure for critical stringer length given above related to horizontal carriage. For a fixed length the pressure gradient for a downward movement must be increased beyond that for horizontal movement by an amount which is proportional to the water-oil density difference and to the angle of slope of the flow lines. In terms of the previous nomenclature, $\alpha l - gl \sin\theta(\rho_w - \rho_o) = 2T(1/r - 1/R)$, r and R being, respectively, the radii of curvature at the leading and rear ends, while θ is the inclination of the flow lines.

The interfacial forces, which resist an increase in the curvature of oil or gas globules and are mobilized in globule motion through a sand of uniform grain size, become even more important when an attempt is made to force these globules from a coarse sand into a finer sand, both sands being water-wet. The resistance, due to interfacial tension, which is opposed to the passage of oil or gas globules from the pores of a coarse sand to the pores of a fine sand or of a clay or shale, provides a filtration effect. This filtering is complete unless the applied force exceeds a certain critical value, which depends on the sizes of the two sets of pores, on the interfacial tension between the oil and water, and on the direction of movement. The force tending to drive the globules into finer pores is supplied by buoyancy, or moving water, or direct squeezing, or by a combination of these three factors. This phenomenon has been well displayed in experiments described by Illing,[6] and the influence of coarseness on oil accumulation in Nature can be observed on both small and large scales. Evidence of the pressure differences associated with the entry of oil into water-wet sands of different sizes has also been given. These experimental data are in agreement with the hypothesis which has formed the basis of the present discussion, namely, that interfacial forces and the fluid which wets the mineral particles, together with the pore and throat sizes and shapes, play an important part in determining the resting-place of oil and gas.

Primary migration

Several agents have been proposed as being the causes of primary migration. These are buoyancy, interfacial tension, and fluids set in motion by compaction.

Oil and gas are formed in sediments which are laid down in water and which are considered to be wetted by water. In general the rocks in which oil and gas are found are believed to be water-wet. The Oklahoma City field is an exception, and there the reservoir rock appears to be wetted by the oil; preferential wetting by the crude oil is considered to be due to some special property of the oil. This reservoir rock must have been water-wet originally, and the stage at which it became oil-wet is not known. In some experimental work on methane-water systems in contact with stainless steel, Hough, Rzasa, and Wood[5] observed that for ascending pressures the steel was water-wet up to 2,000 p.s.i. and methane-wet above 10,000 p.s.i.; between these pressures the wetting medium was uncertain. For descending pressures methane-wetting obtained down to 5,000 p.s.i. and water-wetting below 2,000 p.s.i. Possibly such a change could take place in rocks with oil and water, and it might also show hysteresis. In the succeeding discussion the rocks will be assumed to be preferentially wetted by water.

Buoyancy. The buoyant rise of oil or gas masses in water in rock pores and other openings is not in doubt when these masses have smaller dimensions than the openings through which they have to pass, and similar remarks are applicable to gas masses in oil. No data appear to be available on the sizes of newly formed masses of oil or gas in source rocks if, indeed, they exist in immiscible form in the water in the pores of such rocks. If the parent organic matter is finely macerated and distributed in the source rocks, the initial oil masses, at least, may be expected certainly to be no larger than the particles of organic matter. The liquid masses may, therefore, be of the same order of size as the mineral grains. Gas masses might be somewhat larger than oil masses. As a consequence the newly formed masses of oil and gas may be similar in size to the rock pores. If the globules are greater than the openings connecting the pores, buoyant rise of the isolated masses is improbable because the height of the masses will be too small to cause the required deformation. The basis for this statement resides in the arguments set out in the discussion of 'Some Fundamental Concepts'. Approximate calculations suggest that for globules 'filling' single pores to rise buoyantly, rocks with grains coarser than all except abnormal *reservoir* rocks would be needed.

There are fields in which oil is believed to have migrated downwards from the source to the reservoir rock. Buoyancy would certainly be incapable of causing such migration. Furthermore, if the hydrocarbons originate and undergo primary migration in a 'soluble' form, as has been postulated by some geologists, buoyancy again could not be the motivating force, although compaction could be.

This hypothesis of the migration of oil in a soluble form requires conversion of the oil to droplet form at some stage. Why should this conversion occur only in the reservoir rock?

In the discussion under the heading of 'Some Fundamental Concepts' it was concluded that the finer the rock the taller the oil or gas mass or stringer which would be necessary for buoyant rise. Hence movement by this mechanism would be much more difficult in a shale or clay source rock than in a coarser reservoir rock. The means for transporting isolated globules sufficiently to give the required degree of vertical continuity of the oil or gas in the source rock would surely be capable of carrying the same globules out of the source rock, as indeed it must be if downward migration occurs.

Interfacial tension. A number of the earlier papers on primary migration take note of the fact that the surface tension of water is about two or three times that of crude oil. It is then suggested that as a consequence the water will be drawn into the fine pores of the source rocks while the oil will occupy the larger pores of the reservoir rock. Such a view fails to take note of preferential wetting, the nature of interfacial tension forces, and other factors. Some of the experimental work presented in support of the above hypotheses is ill designed and by no means simulates the conditions which are likely to obtain in Nature. Thus, McCoy and Keyte[10] put an oil-clay mixture in contact with water-saturated sand. The mixture was unnatural and afforded opportunities for the operation of such phenomena as compaction of an *oil-saturated clay* and probably interchange due to preferential wetting. The conditions were, therefore, appreciably different from those which were implicit in the explanations they offered.

It seems most unlikely that interfacial tension in itself would necessarily bring together formerly isolated globules of oil or gas in the source rock, thereby giving sufficient vertical continuity for buoyancy to overcome interfacial forces and carry the oil or gas upwards into a reservoir rock. Furthermore, interfacial tension could not cause the transport of oil or gas if they were in a 'soluble' form. It is difficult to understand how interfacial forces could act on isolated hydrocarbon globules within a mass of source rock so as to *direct them towards* and transfer them into the reservoir rock. How would these interfacial forces 'know' in which direction a reservoir rock lay? However, in water-wet rocks interfacial forces would assist in driving oil or gas globules across a boundary between fine- and coarse-pored rocks into the coarse rock, provided that the globules had attained a position where they were not entirely surrounded by either type of rock. This transfer would reduce the total surface area and the curvature of the oil globules.

Compaction. Fluid movements or mineral grain adjustments during compaction appear to be the only means capable of having the necessary directing (and transporting) effect on hydrocarbons inside a source rock. Compaction is a phenomenon which must take place in fine-grained rocks such as clays or shales, and in the course of burial very considerable volumes of water are expressed from these sediments. Figs. 36 and 37 (Appendix I) give some indication of the magnitude of the volumes of water which may be so expressed.[4] Thus 8 litres may be forced from a 1-cm.^{2} column of sediment which initially was 200 m. thick; this is equal to a 1-cm.^{2} column of water 80 m. tall, and is equivalent to the complete displacement of all the water originally present in a sediment column well over 80 m. thick. All this water passes through the topmost layer of sediment, but at successively lower points progressively smaller volumes of water will pass. If oil formation occurs soon after sedimentation and the movement of water influences the movement of oil and gas, the chances of carrying the oil or gas out of the source rock by compaction will be much greater than if its formation is long delayed. The same conclusion will apply if the hydrocarbon movement is caused by direct squeezing as indicated in the following paragraphs.

If there is an open mesh of platy mineral grains enclosing a pore which in addition to water contains an oil globule, the following events may occur when the globule is not capable of passing undeformed through the throats leading from the pore. When further contraction of the mesh of mineral grains takes place in the course of compaction the pore will decrease in size, water being expelled at first, but eventually the oil globule will begin to be deformed. This will increase its curvature at certain points by compression, a process which will automatically involve increases in curvature at other points, withdrawal at some places, and advance at others, transfer of fluid taking place in an endeavour to keep the surface area at a minimum value and the curvature the same at all points.

Ultimately the globule may be squeezed from the pore into an adjacent pore (Fig. 17), with some counterflow of water to occupy the space vacated by the globule. Some degree of freedom, flexibility, or brittleness of the plates seems likely to render visualization of the detailed mechanics of the process simpler. Thus, the passage onwards of the globule is the result of squeezing it, if this is the correct explanation, and will be a much more jerky process than the expulsion of water. How far the oil will on an average keep pace with the general water movement is uncertain, but there seems to be the possibility of some lag.

The fluid expressed by compaction will move in whatever direction gives pressure relief, i.e. the direction of movement is the path of least resistance. Generally, this will be upwards, but under certain circumstances it can be downwards locally. Thus upward or downward primary migration would be possible by this means.

It is probable that the value of the viscosity of the oil is not of parti-

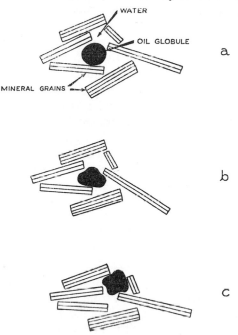

FIG. 17. Suggested sequence of events during squeezing out of an oil globule surrounded by water in a mesh of platy mineral grains which is undergoing compaction.

cular importance at this stage in the process of oil migration. However, when the oil has been aggregated into large masses the ratio of the forces involving viscosity to those dependent on interfacial phenomena will be much greater than for small masses for a given rate of movement, and then the rate of movement will be influenced importantly by the value of the viscosity.

Many years ago, in association with Illing, experimental work on primary oil migration was carried out. In this work mud with a small amount of oil dispersed by shaking was put in a centrifuge tube, and a little compaction induced by centrifuging gently. A thin layer of coarse silica flour was then carefully put on top of the mud, followed by sand, these materials being kept saturated with water. A further layer of silica flour and then oil-free mud were added on top, after which the tube was again centrifuged. In the compaction which ensued oil was carried into the sand and trapped below the capping layer of silica flour. The rate of flow of the compaction currents engendered by the centrifuging was far higher than the rates likely to obtain in Nature. Hence at present the experiments can be interpreted only as indicating qualitatively the feasibility of primary migration by compaction, unless the dominant mechanism is direct squeezing of the hydrocarbon globules as distinct from some form of transport by the moving water.

Subsequently oil-bearing muds were placed in vertical tubes. Layers of silica flour, sand, more silica flour, and mud were added as before, but the final loading was by cylindrical bags of lead shot. No very definite results were observed, but a few globules of oil at the walls of the glass tubes were seen to be elongated, suggesting, though not proving absolutely, that there was relative upward oil movement.

Secondary migration

In compaction with upward flow the rate of water movement and the volume passing will be greater in the upper than in the lower part of the compacting series, while the distance the hydrocarbons must move to leave the top of the source rock will be shorter. Hence, if globules of oil or gas are transported by water movement they will be more likely to be carried from the upper than from the lower parts of the source rock. Should the compaction currents locally be moving downwards, comparable remarks apply, with the ease of globule movement again increasing in the direction of flow. If hydrocarbon globule movement in the source rock takes place by squeezing of the globules by mineral grains the globules in the upper part of the source rock are more likely to be forced from the source rock than are those in the lower part for upward migration. The reverse will be true for downward migration.

Whether or not oil globules will come together to any appreciable extent during movement through the source rock is debatable. Any marked channelling in an even-grained source rock, with lateral feed of globules into the channels, might cause strings of globules to come together. If there is coalescence of any such strings of globules it is possible that relatively large masses of oil (compared with the general sizes of the pores of the source rock) would be forced from the source rock into the reservoir rock. These masses would stay at the point of entry until forced onwards with coalescence by the entry of further masses. On the other hand, if there are only minute hydrocarbon globules at all times in the source rock they may be expected, on entering the reservoir rock, because of the relatively large sizes of the reservoir rock pores, to rise essentially vertically by buoyancy to the upper surface of the reservoir rock in the case of upward primary migration, being stopped there by the cap-rock. Lodged in this position the globules will be joined by others, with presumably coalescence. In the first case when the mass formed by coalescence in the lower part of the reservoir rock is of sufficient height or lateral extent, i.e. has a suitable vertical difference between the highest and lowest points of the connected mass, it will be able to rise upwards in the reservoir rock by buoyancy. Oil reaching the upper surface of the reservoir rock will also rise obliquely in that rock by a comparable mechanism if the upper surface of the reservoir rock is inclined. These movements could take place with or without the aid of hydraulic currents due to compaction or due to artesian conditions, although the critical sizes of the hydrocarbon masses needed for movement to take place would differ in the two cases. Alternatively, hydraulic currents could be the prime movers in the further transport, the final direction of oil movement being dependent on the relative magnitudes and directions of hydraulic and buoyant forces. This is the phase known as secondary migration, and it plays an important part in determining both the extent of segregation of oil, gas, and water, and the site of the final accumulation.

Should tiny globules entering the reservoir rock lodge at some point below the top, accretion will ensue as before when more globules enter, and ultimately the conditions favouring secondary migration may be satisfied as indicated above. For downward primary migration it is logical to expect that the initial lodging-place of the hydrocarbons will be in the upper part of the reservoir rock. Again, when the hydrocarbon mass in the reservoir rock has attained a sufficient height it will move as previously described, provided that comparable conditions hold.

When water is being squeezed by compaction from a series of alternating clays and sands, such as might constitute an oil-bearing sequence with source rocks, reservoir rocks, and cap-rocks, the flow lines will deviate from the vertical in places if the beds are not horizontal. This tendency will be most marked in the highly permeable beds which can serve as reservoir rocks, and will take the form of some deflexion of the flow lines towards the local structurally highest part of the permeable rock. This deflexion may be expected to be strongest in what is, at any time during the formation of the sedimentary sequence, the reservoir rock with the least cover of low permeability potential cap-rock, because the latter may show relatively greater variations in thickness than does the total cover over a deeper permeable rock. These deflected water currents would favour the transport of oil and gas in the reservoir rock towards the local highs. Hence, if oil is formed very early, highs present in the reservoir beds at an early date will become the sites of accumulations, because this stronger deflexion and the more rapid flow than later, in conjunction with other factors, will be especially favourable for upward carriage of oil. The later structural history of the area will determine whether or not the early accumulation is permanent.

Oilfields exist in which the source and reservoir rocks are probably the same. This may be the case for some limestone fields. The stages of migration previously discussed will be modified accordingly, and the equivalent of secondary migration will be dominant.

There has been discussion about the possibility of long-distance lateral migration, as distinct from short-distance lateral migration. Even the most ardent believers in restricted lateral migration would not deny that some lateral migration has taken place in forming an anticlinal accumulation, for example. If the conditions which are necessary for short-distance lateral migration continue to be satisfied it is illogical to deny that lateral migration can take place over considerable distances.

Admission of the feasibility of the rise of suitably sized oil and gas masses by virtue of buoyancy raises the possibility of a considerable amount of secondary migration by circulatory movements, thereby not requiring the continuous onward passage of comparatively large volumes of water. This removes some of the difficulties which would otherwise exist, particularly with respect to adjustments subsequent to the formation of the initial oil accumulation.

It appears probable that deeper burial by virtue of two effects will favour the action of buoyancy in migration and accumulation. The entry of gas into solution under increased pressure will reduce the density of the oil; at constant temperature this is accompanied by an increase in interfacial tension until all the gas is dissolved, then further pressure increase reduces interfacial tension. Rise in temperature reduces the interfacial tension (it may not offset the rise in interfacial tension as the amount of gas in solution is increased) and density. Even when there is no passage of gas into solution it seems likely that the reduction of density of the oil on deeper burial will be greater than for the water, thereby increasing the density difference. If there should also be breakdown of the oil with age or depth of burial this would be a further cause of a greater density difference between oil and water.

It will be apparent that an increase in the tilt of the beds might lead to the aggregation of oil and gas masses which had previously been of insufficient vertical extent, i.e. difference in level between the highest and lowest points, to permit the main phase of secondary migration. Delayed or renewed migration might be explained in this way; it is merely an adjustment in response to a disturbance of the former equilibrium.

The loss of oil and gas by a surface seepage is a further example of migration due to the disturbance of former equilibrium, but the detailed mechanism may differ from that described above.

There is the possibility that under certain circumstances gas might be aggregated into an accumulation without any marked aggregation of oil. This could be caused by the greater density difference between gas and water than between oil and water not being offset by the surface tension between gas and water exceeding the interfacial tension between oil and water.

The comparative cleanness of the sands some distance from an oil accumulation may be a result of bacterial clean-up in which isolated globules and other small detached oil masses are consumed by hydrocarbon-destroying bacteria. If bacterial clean-up is admitted, the conditions must be suitable for the existence of bacteria, and therefore it could be argued that the lapse of time since formation of the sediments, the temperature, and the pressure might not have been unfavourable for any bacteria which might have been capable of forming hydrocarbons. It is probable that carbon dioxide will be formed when bacteria destroy hydrocarbons, and this will increase the solvent power of the brine in the reservoir rock. As a consequence calcium carbonate may be dissolved.

It must also be remembered that although oil has moved through the reservoir rock to form the accumulation, in much of that rock there has probably never been even a moderate concentration of oil, so that the chances of observing oil in cores of such zones would be small, even if there is no bacterial clean-up. Hence zones of reservoir rock which show significant oil impregnation or staining, but which now yield only water, most likely represent places from which much of a former oil accumulation has moved by one or other of several possible processes.

As oil and gas become segregated from water in the reservoir rock they will greatly reduce the permeability to water of the zone in which they have accumulated. Indeed, when the concentration has reached a point at which the interstitial water is approaching or has reached the irreducible minimum the water permeability will approach zero. Hence the highest point at which water passes in bulk into the cap-rock (if that is the means of escape) from the reservoir rock in some structures will change as more and more oil and gas accumulate. This may be associated with a change in the properties of the cap-rock.

The time for the formation of an oil accumulation involves three phases: (*a*) the time from the deposition of the sediment with a suitable organic content on the sea floor to the formation of oil and gas; (*b*) the time for transfer of oil and gas from the source to the reservoir rock by compaction; and (*c*) the time for the aggregation and segregation of the oil and gas in a trap in the reservoir rock. Phases (*a*) and (*b*) may overlap in some measure, and phases (*b*) and (*c*) may overlap to a considerable extent, but because of the comparative slowness of compaction the migration phases of oil accumulation may easily be much longer drawn out than the process of oil formation. Indeed, if oil formation were a geologically long process, the source rocks would have become so compacted that it would be difficult to visualize an adequate phase of primary migration, because the remaining volume of expressible fluid would be relatively small, and the rates of movement would have greatly diminished (Fig. 37).

Levorsen[8] brought forward an ingenious argument in order to ascertain the time of migration for the Oklahoma City oilfield. In this it was argued that the volume of the known oil and gas accumulation at the low pressure which would have obtained before deep burial of the structure would have been many times greater than the storage capacity of the structure at that time. Consequently much of the gas and probably much of the oil could have entered the trap only at a relatively late date (unless the gas was generated from the oil at a late date). This is an interesting example of the quantitative approach to these difficult problems.

Reasons for imperfect segregation. It has frequently been stated that in some areas there has been little segregation of oil because the oil is very viscous. The more likely explanation of this condition is the high density and therefore the inferior buoyancy of the oil. High viscosity would make the rate of movement low, but high density would preclude movement under certain circumstances.

Fig. 18 is based on data tabulated by Muskat[12] (pp. 836–8). The subsurface density has been estimated from the density of the stock-tank oil, the formation volume factor, and the dissolved gas: oil ratio. A broad relationship between subsurface density and subsurface viscosity is indicated, both properties increasing together. A similar relationship may be expected for stock-tank oil densities and viscosities. There are consequently good grounds for noting an *association* between high viscosity and imperfect segregation, but, as suggested above, the more significant factor may be high density.

Examination of data for over thirty fields[12] (p. 104) failed to show any clear relationship between stock-tank oil density and the interfacial tension of the crude against the brine, although Livingston[9] concluded that for five gravity groups using these data the higher the specific gravity values the higher the interfacial tension. The interfacial tension values were measured at atmospheric pressure. The introduction of gas in increasing amounts in solution raises the interfacial tension. This

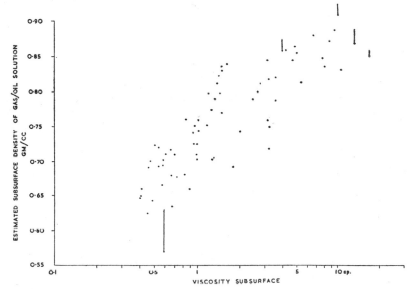

FIG. 18. The dots show the subsurface density values calculated on the assumption that the dissolved gas is methane. The vertical lines show the probable range of densities in a few cases as the gas varies in specific gravity from methane to a decidedly wetter gas.

change is a complex function of the amount of gas dissolved, and the scanty data do not permit generalizations concerning the influence of stock-tank gravity. However, if Livingston's statement holds in general and applies at depth, an association of low interfacial tension with low gravity will be an additional favourable feature for buoyant rise of oil.

Penetration of finer rocks. Earlier discussion has shown that there is a critical height of an oil or gas mass for buoyant rise under 'static' conditions in a water-bearing uniform porous medium. Simple extension of this concept leads to the conclusion that oil or gas masses of suitable height may be able by buoyancy to enter sands or other rocks which are finer-grained than that in which the hydrocarbons originally accumulated (Figs. 19, 20, 21). This condition may arise as the accumulation grows in size in the upper part of the coarse rock. Eventually the

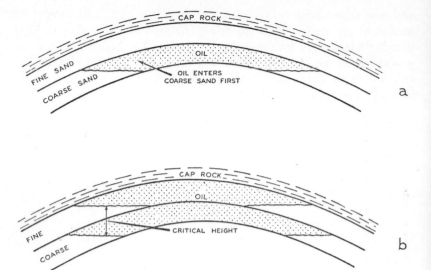

Fig. 19. Successive stages in the build-up of an oil accumulation in sands of different grain sizes. The oil is assumed to enter the coarse sand first; *a*, early stage; *b*, later stage.

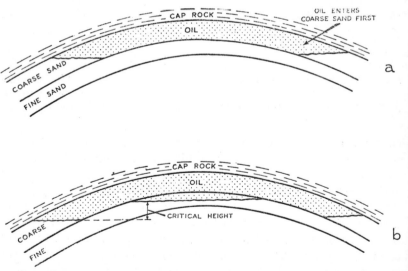

Fig. 20. Successive stages in the build-up of an oil accumulation in sands of different grain sizes. The oil is assumed to enter the coarse sand first: *a*, early stage; *b*, later stage.

hydrocarbons may enter an overlying rather finer sand (Fig. 19), and in principle an accumulation of sufficient height could ultimately penetrate a watered clay or shale cap-rock.

The height of a hydrocarbon mass is fixed by the thickness, porosity, and interstitial water content of the reservoir rocks, the inclination and lateral extent of these rocks, and the quantity of hydrocarbons present. Thus penetration of this kind is most likely in steeply dipping rocks comprising zones of different grain sizes, these zones not being individually thick. On the other hand, in flat-lying beds the influence of

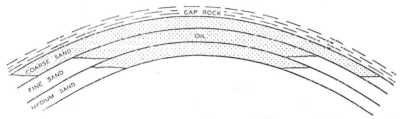

FIG. 21. Distribution of oil in sand layers of different grain sizes.

grain size on the presence or absence of oil will be very marked unless the individual zones are very thick and large amounts of oil are present. Oil and gas columns of considerable height are known: some 2,500 ft. of gas and 2,000 ft. of oil at Turner Valley; about 2,200 ft. of oil at Masjid-i-Sulaiman. Reliable figures for the sizes of the interstices in clays and shales are not available, but if they are 0.1μ wide and the underlying sand is of 0.05 cm. grain size, the pressure for penetration with an oil-water interfacial tension of 20 dynes/cm. would be such as to require a column some 540 m. high if the oil density is 0.85 gm./cm.[3]

Inclined fluid contacts. If there is a change in grain size, then for similar packings there will be a corresponding change in pore size. Change in pore size will automatically fix the minimum curvature of the meniscus of a globule in the pore and, as indicated earlier, the curvature determines the pressure differential across the interface. If the globule fluid is continuously connected between the two points at which pores of different size exist, the differences in the pressure across the menisci at the two points must be offset by differences in elevation, which, in turn, will be affected by the differences in densities of the two fluids. For close-packed uniform spheres of diameter 0.1 mm. at one point, with a density differential of 0.15 gm./c.c., and interfacial tension of 20 dynes/cm., the differences in height for grains of 0.05 mm., 0.02 mm., or 0.01 mm. at the other point will be, respectively, 1.3 m.,

5·3 m., or 11·8 m. In all cases the differences in height refer to the larger pore occupied by a lobe of minimum curvature at each point.

The practical significance of the above inferences is that if a reservoir rock changes gradually in grain size and in pore size laterally, then the general oil-water contact zone will vary in elevation, being higher where the pores are smaller.* Inclined water-tables have been reported in a number of fields, but no example appears to have been described precisely with elevation differences associated with measurements of grain

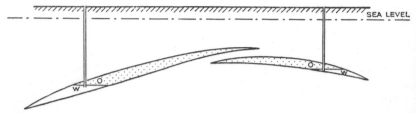

Fig. 22. Apparently inclined oil-water contact, resulting from wells penetrating different sand lenses.

sizes, pore sizes, or capillary pressures. In some cases it is by no means certain that the inclination was original and due to variations in pore size; the possibility exists that the inclination may have developed in the course of production due to non-uniform extraction of oil. Locally water-coning and gas-coning are well-recognized phenomena associated with high producing rates from single wells. Such cones have been inferred to flatten from the well behaviour when the rate of production has subsequently been reduced. This flattening is due to the adjustments caused by the fluid-density differences.

Other factors which need to be considered in examining the reported cases of inclined water-tables are the means whereby the water-table was defined, and whether the observations were made on what was a continuous bed. Fig. 22 shows a case (one of several possibilities) where imperfect knowledge could give an erroneous suggestion of an inclined water-table. Electric logging, drillstem testing, and coring in recent years have provided far more data on reservoir make-up and fluid distribution than could have been obtained in years gone by, and thereby have revealed complexities and details which would of necessity have been missed in the past. Hence there is considerable doubt concerning

* In a recent paper S. T. Yuster (*J. Petrol. Tech.*, May 1953, **5** (5), A.I.M.M.E. Tech. Paper No. 3564, 149–56) has calculated that for a density difference of 0·1 gm./c.c., 20 per cent. porosity, interfacial tension 20 dynes/cm., and a contact angle of 60°, a permeability change from 1,000 mD to 1 mD would involve a rise of 330 ft. for the oil/water contact.

the real explanation of inclined water-tables reported, especially in old oilfields.

The behaviour of the oil-water contact on production must also be considered in attempting to determine the cause of inclined oil-water contacts. If there is no advance the inclination observed may be due to cementation or tar. However, absence of water advance could also be explained by absence of potential water-drive, i.e. the extent of the reservoir rock beyond the hydrocarbon-bearing zone is limited.

In some cases the inclination has been suggested to be the result of regional tilting and insufficient time having elapsed for the oil-water contact, although free, to have adjusted itself once more to horizontality. It is difficult to decide whether the rate of tilting would ever be so rapid that the oil-water contact could not keep substantially in equilibrium, and whether, in any case, equilibrium would necessarily require horizontality.*

If the phenomenon of hysteresis observed in laboratory studies of capillary pressures operates in fluid adjustments in Nature, and is not merely a consequence of the relatively rapid rates of displacement used in the laboratory, it may account in part at least for inclined fluid contacts. Should the oil-water or gas-oil contact become inclined as a result of tilting of the structure the adjustments (actual or potential) at the lower points will be imbibitional, while those at the upper end of the contact will be equivalent to drainage. Laboratory investigations have shown that at a given fluid saturation the capillary pressure is lower for imbibition than for drainage. Hence, in terms of these observations stability would be possible for a limited difference in level between the lowest and highest parts of the inclined contact. For similar reasons asymmetrical feed of oil to an accumulation could also lead to inclined contacts, the term 'asymmetrical' being used here in relation to the combined factors of supply of oil and form of the reservoir rock.

Russell has suggested that the inclination of an oil-water contact may be maintained by the flow of water.[13] In this he visualizes that the oil is kept stationary with its lower surface inclined, and that the product of the difference in elevation between two points and the fluid density difference is equal to the pressure difference between the two points in the water due to flow. (Comparison should be made with the discussion on p. 75, in which allowance is made for the curvatures of the interfaces

* Yuster has concluded, on the basis of certain calculations, that it seems unlikely that the rate of tilting of the formations would ever be such as to create significantly inclined fluid contacts. He has also noted that variations in fluid densities, contact angle, and interfacial tension are among the static factors which could cause inclined fluid contacts.

between the fluids.) The difficulty about Russell's suggestion is that it cannot be used to explain the occurrence of tilted gas-oil and oil-water contacts in the same pool. The tilt of the former would demand that the oil was flowing.

Russell has argued that the maximum hydraulic gradient due to artesian circulation in rocks which may act as oil reservoirs may have been 1 in 500, with the possibility that water currents for 1 ft. in 200 days may have existed. The velocities for compaction currents may normally have been much less than 3 in. per year, a figure similar to the 1 in. per year suggested by McCoy and Keyte from the penetration of fresh-water in some basins. A hydraulic gradient of 1 in 500 would give a slope for the oil-water contact of nearly 1 degree for a density difference of 0·12 gm./c.c. between the water and oil, *if Russell's suggestion applies*. In most cases the slope would be decidedly less than this value, irrespective of any allowance for interfacial phenomena.

In the North Coles Levee field, California, the oil-water contacts reported are lower on the northern flank and eastern nose than in the crestal area.[1] A drop of about 700 ft. occurs, giving a mean slope of about 3 degrees in one direction. Davis states that inclination is not unusual in the Stevens sand fields of the San Joaquin Valley, and it 'is believed to be the result of lenticularity and sedimentation changes in the sands and pronounced changes in permeability'. He also notes that no measurable movement of the oil-water contact has been observed.

Under reservoir conditions the density of the North Coles Levee oil might be 0·58–0·62 gm./c.c. If the formation water is similar to sea-water its density under reservoir conditions might be 0·99 gm./c.c. In terms of Russell's hypothesis a slope of 3 degrees for the oil-water contact would require flow of the water under hydraulic gradients of about 1 in 50. Davis's description of the Stevens sand is certainly not indicative of the possibility of the existence of suitable water flow throughout the sand section which could account for a 3-degree slope. Quite apart from the large value of the hydraulic gradient, a further difficulty is that flow would have to cross low permeability streaks.

Arched oil-water contacts have been described. It is improbable that all such forms are due to flowing water.* Some may be formed partially

* Recently M. K. Hubbert (*Bull. Amer. Assoc. Petrol. Geol.*, Aug. 1953, **37** (8), 1954–2027) has discussed in detail the accumulation of oil and gas under hydrodynamic conditions, i.e. with water flow occurring in the reservoir beds. In this discussion he has indicated means whereby a convex upwards oil-water contact would be possible on an anticlinal structure in a uniform reservoir rock. However, it does not seem possible to adapt his explanations to the case of a concave upwards oil-water contact in an anticlinal accumulation in a uniform reservoir rock. If non-uniformity

or wholly by warping of the structure with restriction of water flow precluding fluid adjustments, unless they are not what they appear to be but are in reality a series of basically independent fluid contacts in a reservoir rock which is composite. There are also reports of basin-shaped fluid contacts.* Again simple flow would not provide a satisfactory explanation.

When a reservoir rock has shale streaks or partings, seemingly odd fluid contacts can occur, and the differences in fluid contact levels may be interpreted as inclined contacts. If the partings are continuous throughout and beyond the hydrocarbon-bearing zone each compartment in the main reservoir rock can have oil-water and gas-oil contacts which differ from those of other compartments (Fig. 23 *a*). Failure to recognize the presence of this condition in a reservoir may lead to the location of wells on the basis of incorrect assumptions, and these wells may give unexpected results. If the partings are less extensive, obviously there can be differences in level only for the fluid contact cut by the parting (Fig. 23 *b* and *c*).

Some structural traps. It has been noted that whether moving water or buoyant rise under 'static' conditions dominates secondary migration, the oil and gas will tend to take the steepest path available locally. Figs. 24, 25, and 26 illustrate the consequences of this tendency when there is general flow of water and hydrocarbons, for a monoclinal dome and for strike faults on a monocline, one fault being down-thrown on the down-dip side, and the other down-thrown on the up-dip side and associated with some warping. Oil and gas will move into the monoclinal dome (Fig. 24), and also into the area of closure down-dip from the fault which is down-thrown on the up-dip side (Fig. 25). On the other hand, there will be no tendency to trap oil and gas when the fault is down-thrown on the down-dip side and associated with a structure of the type shown in Fig. 26.

Displacement. When a series of domes exist at different levels on a monocline the following conditions may arise: If oil and gas enter the reservoir bed low on the monocline they will migrate upwards to occupy the first dome in their path. If there is sufficient oil and gas the dome

of the reservoir rock is invoked to change the directions of the flow lines and of the equi-potential surfaces, it becomes very difficult to separate inclinations which might be due to hydrodynamic factors from those which may be described as static and due directly to the lithological changes.

* It may be noted that at San Ardo, Salinas Valley, California, a synclinal oil-water contact occurs in the Lombardi sand on a slight arch (T. A. Baldwin, *J. Petrol. Tech.*, Jan. 1953, **5** (1), 9–10). However, the sand wedges out, and this feature would not favour flow. Shale barriers are said to be absent within this sand, and Baldwin attributes the form of the oil-water contact to warping.

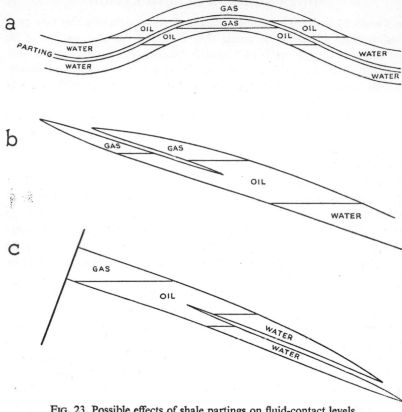

FIG. 23. Possible effects of shale partings on fluid-contact levels.

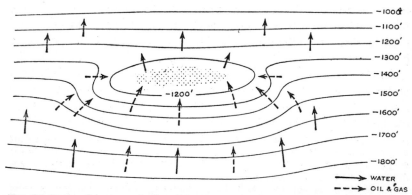

FIG. 24. Paths of water, and oil and gas movement in migration up a monocline on which there is a dome, with formation of an oil and gas accumulation (dotted) in the dome (after Illing[6]). In this figure and in the next two the main fluid flow is assumed to be along the stratum. Such flow is possible under certain conditions.

will eventually be filled with hydrocarbons to the spilling plane, and then further oil migrating upwards will pass on or displace oil which will itself move onwards to escape or to a higher trap. However, gas, if in sufficiently buoyant masses, will still enter the first dome, displacing oil, and should enough gas enter all the oil, except perhaps a small

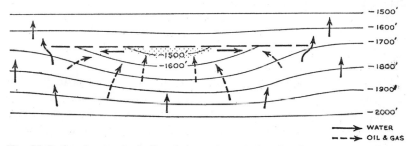

FIG. 25. Paths of water, and oil and gas movements in migration up a monocline on which there is a strike fault down-thrown on the up-dip side. Closure against the fault on the down-dip side gives a dome and local steepening of the dips leading to oil and gas accumulation (after Illing[6]).

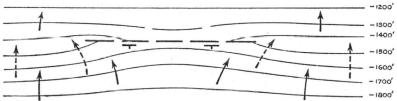

FIG. 26. Paths of water, and oil and gas movement in migration up a monocline on which there is a strike fault down-thrown on the down-dip side. There is no closure against the fault, and steepening of the dip takes the oil and gas past the fault (after Illing[6]). (The arrows have the same significance as in Figs. 24 and 25.)

amount which is largely disconnected, will be displaced and pass on-wards up the monocline.

A comparable series of events may also occur in domes on a mono-cline when oil and gas entry is taking place over a considerable area, and not merely low on the monocline.

Subsequent deeper burial, intensification, or suitable tilting of the structure might leave the significant fluid contact above the level of the current spilling plane, and so mask the former relationship.

Not only may tilting cause the adjustment of fluid contacts, but it may also reduce the structural closure in some cases. If the volume of closure is reduced to a value less than the volume of hydrocarbons present before tilting, some of these will escape. When both oil and free gas are present the oil, being in the lower position, will escape before the free gas. Hence oil with gas in solution, or oil and free gas may be lost from an area of closure as a result of tilting.

Flushing. Although the general conditions for the carriage of oil or gas globules or stringers by hydraulic currents can be defined, only detailed knowledge of the nature and setting of a structure will reveal whether currents possibly having the critical velocity *must have passed through it.* In many cases hydraulic currents may largely have skirted a 'high' and could not be considered, therefore, to have been capable of flushing oil or gas from that structure.

Since areas undergo tilting, and structures may change in form or intensity with time, all cases of supposed downward flushing should be examined carefully to see whether there is reliable evidence of the former existence of a more extensive oil accumulation. Some structural traps may not have existed or may have had a much smaller capacity at the time of oil migration. If there has also been an increase in burial with an associated increase in pressure, much gas may have gone into solution and thereby caused a considerable reduction in the total space occupied by the hydrocarbons. Examination of Fig. 4 will indicate the possibilities in this connexion, and this matter is discussed generally in Chapter V on 'Reservoir Pressure'.

Fluid adjustments associated with faulting. When a reservoir rock containing an oil or gas accumulation is subjected to faulting, redistribution of the fluids may take place if the fracture is open. In considering the possible nature of the adjustments it is essential to note the three-dimensional form of the structure affected, and not merely to make the predictions in terms of a single section. It is assumed in the following discussion that the open fracture does not give access to the surface, since such access would lead to partial or complete loss of the oil and gas.

Figs. 27 *b* and *c* represent successive stages in the adjustment of the fluids originally in the unfaulted dome shown in Fig. 27 *a*, in response to increasing fault displacement. The perspective sketch (Fig. 27 *d*), corresponding to the section in Fig. 27 *b*, shows the lateral communications which permit water to be transferred to the down-thrown block at a low level while oil passes to the up-thrown block at higher levels. The section in Fig. 27 *b* does not show the communications available to the water, and at first sight may appear to present a condition in which it would be impossible for water to reach the down-thrown block because of the intervening rise in the base of the reservoir rock in the section.

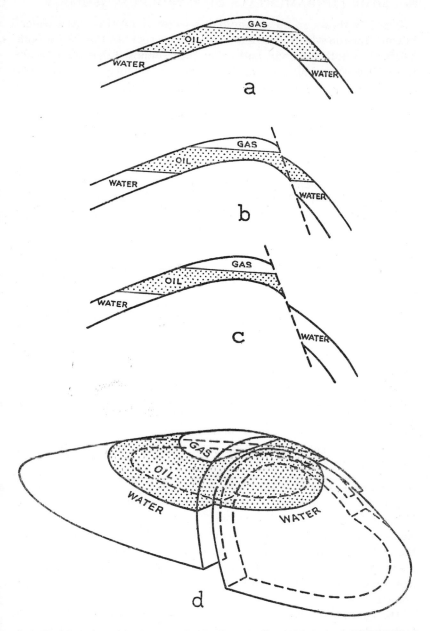

FIG. 27. Successive stages in the redistribution of oil and gas as a result of faulting.

Fig. 28 *a* shows an oil accumulation which is overlain by a water-bearing horizon which could act as a reservoir rock. In Fig. 28 *b* a fault has broken both horizons, and it has been supposed that the fracture was sufficiently open to permit fluid interchange between the two horizons. As a result oil and gas have, by buoyancy, moved into the upper

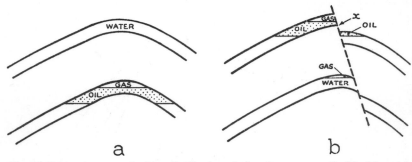

a   b

FIG. 28. Successive stages in the redistribution of oil and gas as a result of faulting and circulation of fluids via the fault.

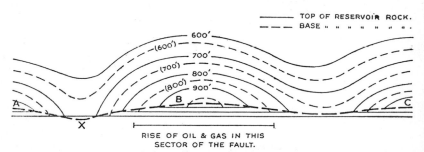

FIG. 29. Faulted domes to which oil and gas are assumed to gain access initially via the fault and subsequently by lateral movement under the spilling planes in the saddles.

horizon, while water has gone from the upper horizon to the lower horizon. Some gas has remained in the lower horizon because there is slight arching of the top of the bed, giving a closed zone from which the hydrocarbons cannot escape by upward movement. The beds are assumed to be arched in a direction normal to the section shown, and hence water has been able to leave the upper bed at a level below the point x.

The stratum contours in Fig. 29 define the up-thrown sector of a faulted dome with parts of two adjacent domes, also affected by the same fault. If oil and gas rise up the sector marked opposite dome *B*, and do not go above the horizon contoured, they will enter the reservoir rock in dome B. This dome will be filled with hydrocarbons from the top downwards until the hydrocarbon-water contact is slightly below 800 ft., at which time hydrocarbons will begin to spill under the top of the saddle between domes B and C if more oil and gas enter dome B. Dome C will be filled from the top downwards by this lateral transfer, and provided there is no spill-under surface bounding dome C at a level higher than the point of entry between B and C, dome C can be filled down to the level of entry. Further additions of oil and gas to dome B will increase the accumulation in both domes (B and C). If dome C has no exit higher than the top of the saddle between domes B and A, the continued entry of oil and gas into dome B will eventually lead to the filling of domes B and C to a level just below 700 ft., after which hydrocarbons would spill laterally into dome A. The subsequent developments will be apparent from what has been described above.

If x is the position of the lowest spill-over point for water in this series of interconnected structures, that will fix the level to which the hydrocarbon-water contact would fall by hydrocarbon and water interchange via the fault. Pressure, temperature, and other changes subsequent to the end of entry of oil and gas to these domes could change oil and water contacts, and so mask initial relationships which might have served as a guide to the mode of formation of the group of accumulations.

It is also possible for dome B to have far more gas (free gas) than domes A and C. This would be because in the earlier stages oil, but no free gas, would spill under the saddles to domes A and C. The drop in pressure suffered by the oil in rising to the crests of domes A and C could lead to the evolution of some gas from solution, thereby forming a gas cap. However, the relative sizes of the gas caps and the position of the gas-oil contact need not be the same in domes A and C as in dome B. Later changes in depth of burial could cause changes in the positions of the fluid levels and in the amount of free gas.

The preceding discussion has shown that the final resting-place of an oil and gas accumulation is dependent on a series of factors. These include the properties of the reservoir rock and its structural form, not only now but at all times subsequent to the formation of the oil. The site of the accumulation is, in fact, dependent on the stratigraphic and structural history of the area.

REFERENCES

1. DAVIS, C. A., *J. Petrol. Tech.*, **4** (8), 11–21 (1952).
2. CRAZE, R. C., ibid., **2** (10), 289 (1950).

3. GRATON, L. C., and FRASER, H. J., *J. Geol.*, **43**, 785–909 (1935).
4. HOBSON, G. D., *J. Inst. Pet.*, **29**, 37–54 (1943).
5. HOUGH, E. W., RZASA, M. J., and WOOD, B. B., *J. Petrol. Tech.*, **3** (2), A.I.M.M.E. Tech. Paper No. 3019 (1951).
6. ILLING, V. C., *J. Inst. Pet. Tech.*, **19**, 229–60 (1933); **25**, 201–25 (1939).
7. —— *The Science of Petroleum*, i, 209–15, Oxford University Press, 1938.
8. LEVORSEN, A. I., *Bull. Amer. Assoc. Petrol. Geol.*, **29**, 1189–94 (1945).
9. LIVINGSTON, H. K., *Petrol. Tech.*, **1**, A.I.M.M.E. Tech. Pub. No. 1001 (1938).
10. McCOY, A. W., and KEYTE, W. R., *Problems of Petroleum Geology*, 252–307, Amer. Assoc. Petrol. Geol., 1934.
11. MEINZER, O. E., and WENZEL, L. K., *Physics of the earth. IX, Hydrology*, 449, McGraw-Hill Book Co. Inc., 1942.
12. MUSKAT, M., *Physical Principles of Oil Production*, 104, 836–8, McGraw-Hill Book Co. Inc., 1949.
13. RUSSELL, W. L., *Principles of Petroleum Geology*, McGraw-Hill Book Co. Inc., 1951.

V

RESERVOIR PRESSURE

FLOWING oil-wells, and the spectacular 'gushers' of bygone years, clearly indicate that the fluids in the reservoir rock are stored under pressure. This pressure has been variously referred to as formation pressure, reservoir pressure, and rock pressure. The last expression has sometimes been used in a different sense from the above by some geologists and civil engineers, and since the words 'rock' and 'formation' are often interchangeable the use of the first expression might be challenged. Consequently 'reservoir pressure' will be used in the following discussion.

Reservoir pressure and its origin are of general interest as well as of practical importance in oil production. In order to extract oil from a reservoir rock with maximum 'efficiency', having due regard to economic as well as technical considerations, it is necessary to ascertain at an early stage in the development of an oilfield the real seat of the reservoir pressure.

Instruments are available for making pressure measurements in wells, and it has been observed that the reservoir pressure falls in many oilfields as oil is extracted. A similar drop may occur in the exploitation of gasfields. In attempting to determine some of the fundamental factors concerned in the origin of reservoir pressure it is necessary to use the virgin reservoir pressure—the reservoir pressure which obtained before any appreciable fraction of the recoverable oil or gas reserve had been taken from the reservoir.

When fluid flows through a reservoir rock into a well it does so because there is a pressure gradient towards the well, i.e. the pressure at the well is lower than at a point some distance from the well. If the flow from the well at the surface is stopped by closing the valves there will be pressure adjustments within the reservoir and the well. Because it is compressible fluid will flow towards and into the well bore until the pressure gradient vanishes as a consequence of this fluid transfer. The period of adjustment may be long in some cases, as when the rock permeability is low, the fluid viscosity high, and the pressure difference large at the time the well is closed in. The pressure changes at the bottom of the well after closing it are referred to as the pressure build-up; they may not be complete after a month or more, or they may be complete in a few hours, depending on conditions. The pressure reached when fluid transfer has ended is the fully built-up closed-in pressure. Unless otherwise stated, fully built-up closed-in pressures will alone be considered in the following pages.

Elementary consideration of the laws of hydrostatics shows that at

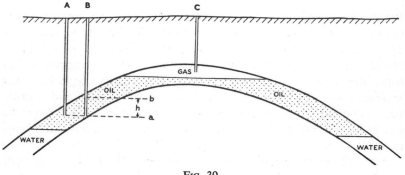

FIG. 30.

the bottom of wells A and B (Fig. 30), i.e. at the horizontal plane represented by a, the pressures on the oil will be the same provided that no flow is taking place. At the horizontal plane labelled b the pressure on the oil will be less than at a; the difference in pressure will be equal to $h\rho_0$, where ρ_0 is the mean density of the oil between planes a and b, and h is the difference in level of these two planes. In most cases, and provided that the distance between a and b is not great, the density of the oil between the two planes can be taken to be constant. The pressure measured in the gas cap at the bottom of well C will be less than at plane b by an amount dependent on the distance of b below the gas-oil contact, plus an amount dependent on the distance of the bottom of well C above the same contact, and on the density of the gas. In a gas cap of considerable height the gas density, although low, may vary appreciably with elevation.

As mentioned above, the pressure values measured will be dependent on the elevation of the point of measurement. Hence, in order to eliminate differences due to this factor, and thereby to throw into relief differences due to other causes, e.g. different reservoirs, fault, or permeability barriers, it is customary to adjust the observations under study to a common datum. For some purposes a datum is selected within the known oil column. However, in some fundamental studies a datum in the water zone must be used. For observations made above the datum an addition will be made which will be the product of the elevation difference and the appropriate fluid density; for observations below the datum subtraction will be made of a pressure similarly determined.

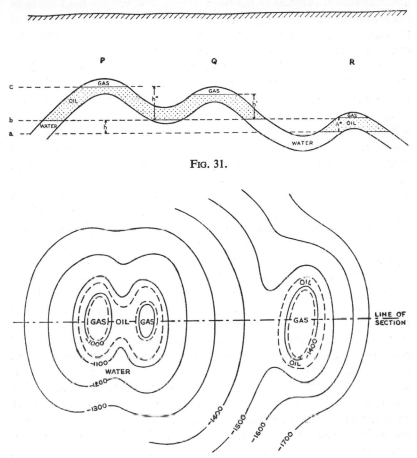

FIG. 31.

FIG. 32. Stratum contour map showing lateral water communications which are available for the structure shown in cross-section in Fig. 31.

Pressure: depth ratio

Fig. 31 is a section drawn through three domes. Because of the form of the structure there will be a continuous oil-water contact encircling dome *P* and also dome *Q* (see Fig. 32), and since the lowest part of the top of the reservoir rock in the intervening syncline or saddle is above the oil-water level, both domes have the same oil-water level. The different oil-water contact in dome R is possible because the reservoir rock top in the saddle separating dome R from dome Q is lower than the oil-water contacts. A comparable feature permits the existence of different gas-oil contacts in the three domes. The various fluid contacts are assumed to be horizontal. The domed structure allows continuity of the water around the flanks from the left flank of dome P to the saddle between domes Q and R, and thence to the right flank of dome R. Hence pressure measurements made at any common level in the water in these three features will be identical; in particular there will be identicality of the pressure at level a (Fig. 31), which corresponds with the oil-water contact of dome R. At level b, which is a distance h above level a, the pressure will be $p-h\rho_w$ in domes P and Q, and $p-h\rho_o$ in dome R, where p is the common pressure at level a, and ρ_w and ρ_o are, respectively, the densities of the water and oil. Since $\rho_w > \rho_o$, $p-h\rho_o$ will be greater than $p-h\rho_w$, i.e. the pressure at level b in dome R will be greater than in domes P and Q. At level c the pressures will be $p-h\rho_w-h\rho_o$ (dome P), and $p-h\rho_w-h'\rho_o-(h''-h')\rho_g$ (dome Q), ρ_g being the gas density, and the oil densities being assumed to be the same in domes P, Q, and R. It is evident that the pressures at level c will increase in going from dome P to dome Q, and the gas-cap pressures will increase in the order P, Q, R.

From the foregoing discussion it can be deduced that identicality of pressures at a fixed level in a given fluid points to, although it does not prove, the existence of a permeable connexion between the various places of measurement through the fluid in question; pressure differences at a fixed level in a given fluid demonstrate the absence of such a connexion through that fluid between the places of measurement. Reasons are also afforded for making comparisons of observations at different levels or in different fluids. It is also apparent that separation of the three gas caps in Fig. 31 could have been inferred from pressure measurements made in wells which had penetrated the gas zones only, and had not penetrated any of the various gas-oil contacts, penetration of which would, because of level differences of these contacts, have proved the same point (assuming that there is not an inclined fluid contact).

Fig. 33 is a section through an oil and gas accumulation. The topography is assumed to be horizontal and the oil-water contact is at a depth H, at which level the pressure is P. The height of the oil column of density ρ_o is h_o, and the height of the gas cap of density ρ_g is h_g. The pressure at the gas-oil contact will be $P-h_o.\rho_o$; the pressure at the top of the gas cap will be $P-h_o.\rho_o-h_g.\rho_g$. For the three levels mentioned the ratios of pressure to depth will be, respectively, P/H, $P-h_o.\rho_o/H-h_o$, and $P-h_o.\rho_o-h_g.\rho_g/H-h_o-h_g$.

On the right and left of the cross-section in Fig. 33 are pressure-depth diagrams illustrative of two of the pressure distributions which could exist. On the right the pressure at the oil-water contact has been made considerably greater than on the left. On the right the mean pressure gradient from the oil-water contact to the surface is greater than the pressure gradients in either the oil or gas zones. Inspection therefore reveals that the pressure: depth ratio for observations made in the fluids above this point will be greater than the mean pressure gradient mentioned above, and it will become greater the shallower the point considered. In contrast, inspection of the left-hand diagram shows that for

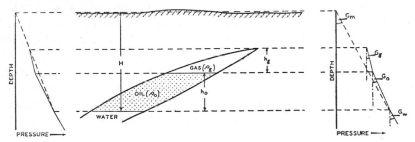

FIG. 33. The mean pressure gradient and the pressure gradients in the gas, oil, and water zones are given, respectively, by the tangents of the angles G_m, G_g, G_o, and G_w.

measurements within the oil zone the ratio would be smaller at shallower depths, but on entering the gas zone it would increase as the depth decreased. Had the gas zone been appreciably thicker the ratio for the shallowest depths would have been greater than the mean gradient to the oil-water contact.

The preceding remarks show that the pressure: depth ratio (average pressure gradient) is a function of the depth of measurement, and of the heights, positions, and densities of the various fluids.

Before examining the possible significance of the values of the pressure: depth ratio, reference must be made to differences in ground elevation in a single oilfield. If the datum pressure for each well is associated with the individual well depth, then, even if that pressure were constant, depth variations from the ground surface to the datum, due to topographical irregularities, would cause differences in the pressure: depth ratios. General considerations indicate that these differences must be eliminated in fundamental studies, and therefore it is customary for the depth measurement to be made from some arbitrary level such as the mean surface elevation or sometimes sea-level. It will be seen later that in some instances neither of these levels need have any particular significance relative to the subsurface pressure values.

It is not possible to apply checks to some of the older published pressure data. Details of the methods of measurement and of the state of the wells or fields at the time of measurement are lacking; whether the pressures were observed in or adjusted to the gas, oil, or water zones is not known; and the precise implications of the reported depths are uncertain. Accordingly, in discussing such data it can only be assumed that they satisfy some of the requirements which have been indicated in the preceding paragraphs.

The pressure in the water zone would seem to be of most importance from many points of view, and so the value at the oil-water contact might be most appropriate. A pressure:depth ratio equivalent to a column of water would then be suggestive of reservoir pressure determined by water extending through the rock pores from the field surface to the water zone in the reservoir rock, *with no fluid flow due to compaction taking place*, i.e. the pressure is hydrostatic. (Equilibrium between the gas-cap pressure and the water column in the rocks over the top of the structure will be attained via curvature of fluid interfaces, and comparable remarks apply to the oil zone.)

Comparisons of reservoir pressures and depths have been made, and broadly it has been found that the pressures are higher the deeper the reservoirs, but there are numerous exceptions. Instances have been quoted of multiple reservoir fields in which a shallow reservoir may have a higher pressure than a deeper reservoir. The ratio of pressure to depth has also been studied, and considerable variations in the pressure:depth gradient have been noted. However, there is a tendency for the values of this gradient to cluster around a figure which is characteristic of a column of water, i.e. 0·43 p.s.i./ft.

Examination of what appear to be some of the more reliable published data on reservoir pressures shows a range of pressure:depth values from 0·224 to 0·99 p.s.i./ft., the latter value being estimated for Khaur in Pakistan.

The lowest pressure:depth ratio encountered in searching the literature was for a Trenton gas well in the vicinity of Cleveland, Ohio.[7] The gas flow was small and the highest pressure observed was 37 p.s.i. for a depth of 4,445 ft. Even if it is assumed that this is a closed-in well-head pressure the subsurface gas pressure would be little more than 40 p.s.i. (Van Horn[7] does not record details of the pressure measurement). After making this allowance the pressure:depth ratio would still be less than 0·01 p.s.i./ft.

Fig. 34 shows the distribution of the values of the pressure: depth ratio for about 160 observations taken from over 100 fields or areas. It has been assumed that the data approach the ideal requirements, but it has not been feasible to check this. Some degree of estimation has been necessary in adapting some of the figures. Eighty per cent. of the values

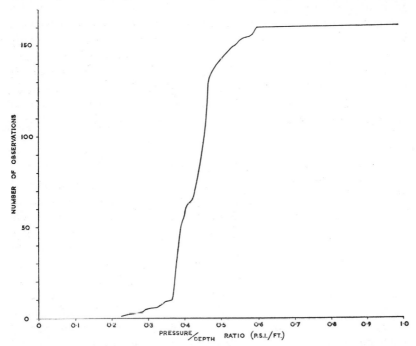

Fig. 34. The pressure : depth ratios are for fields in U.S.A., Venezuela, and Pakistan. The information is given in the form of a cumulative curve.

are between 0·366 and 0·508 p.s.i./ft., and the middle 50 per cent. ranges 0·382–0·463 p.s.i./ft. The bias in favour of values below 0·43 p.s.i./ft. in the last case is due in part to the inclusion of a considerable number of observations from the Greater Oficina area, where twenty-eight observations ranged 0·363–0·392 p.s.i./ft. Eighty per cent. of the observations taken from Muskat's data[4] are in the range 0·362–0·468 p.s.i./ft., and 50 per cent. in the range 0·392–0·462 p.s.i./ft.

Hydrostatic head

When the reservoir rock has a continuation which outcrops, then if water is entering the outcrop or spilling from the outcrop, the outcrop level will fix the reservoir pressure (apart from a small factor dependent on the rate of flow and permeability), and the pressure can again be claimed to be hydrostatic. In this case the ratio of pressure to depth in the field need not approximate to 0·43 p.s.i./ft., but the ratio of the pressure to the *depth below the outcrop of the reservoir rock* should approximate to this figure.

It is evident from what has been written above that unless the relevant values are used in investigating the relationship between pressure and depth there could be failure to recognize that the pressure is hydrostatic in origin. In particular it must be recalled that even though the reservoir pressure is of hydrostatic origin, pressure:depth ratios for points in the oil or gas columns could, under certain circumstances, exceed 0·43 p.s.i./ft.

Compaction

Suppose that fluid is stored in a container under a pressure of P_i. If the walls are impermeable to the fluid and, by the application of external pressure, the volume of storage space in the container is reduced, the fluid pressure will rise. The rise in pressure will be determined by the reduction in storage space and by the compressibility of the fluid; low compressibilities will be associated with large rises in pressure, and large compressibilities with small rises in pressure. If the walls are not impermeable the pressure rises will be smaller in magnitude for the following reasons. In a given time the volume of the storage space is reduced from V to $V-dV$, and during the same time a mass of fluid dm leaves the container. If dm is less than the mass of fluid which under pressure P_i would occupy a volume dV the final pressure will exceed P_i; if dm would be of volume dV at P_i there will be no pressure change. If initially the quantity which escapes is less than would be equivalent in volume to dV at P_i, but after cessation of diminution of the storage space there is continued escape of fluid until an amount equivalent to dV at P_i has gone, there will be a concomitant gradual decline of the pressure to the value which obtained before the storage space began to be reduced. Should fluid be squeezed into storage space of fixed volume there will be a rise in pressure.

Brief consideration shows that some or all of the conditions envisaged in the last paragraph can obtain in some measure in a series of compacting sediments, whether the compaction is due simply to the weight of the sediments or is being effected to some extent by lateral pressure due to orogeny. In simple compaction, without complications due to deposition of cement or to recrystallization, a reservoir rock such as a sand will constitute a container of substantially fixed volume of storage space. The adjacent shales or clays will be diminishing in bulk volume and therefore in storage space. Hence there will be a tendency for fluids to be squeezed from them. Consequently the pressure on the fluids in these fine-grained sediments will be above hydrostatic, and this will affect the pressure in contiguous sands. When the compaction is due solely to the load of sediments above the reservoir there will be an upper limit, for a given depth, to the possible pressures on the fluids in the clays and shales, and hence to the reservoir pressure; this limiting pressure will be equal to the pressure caused by the rock load. The rock load pressure will be of the order of 1 p.s.i./ft. If the escape of fluid (i.e. the volume of the mass escaping, measured at the initial pressure) fails to keep pace with shrinkage of storage space the fluid will be compressed and there will be a rise in pressure above hydrostatic; but if the amount which escapes becomes equal to storage space shrinkage the pressure will fall to hydrostatic.

When the compaction is caused by lateral pressure the maximum fluid pressure attainable is not so easily defined. The pressure which the formations will withstand without parting or fracturing will constitute a limit which may well exceed the rock load. Again, there will be pressure decline with the passage of time after cessation of compaction if fluid can escape. The ultimate value attained by this decline will be a pressure equal to hydrostatic.

In terms of these mechanisms there will be a tendency for reservoir pressures in many cases to lie between hydrostatic and approximately rock load values. However, if, as a result of cementation, the reservoir is sealed off, subsequent erosion or deposition could cause the pressure to be associated with depths which fail to give pressure:depth ratios characteristic of hydrostatic or rock load control. Thus, by erosion, ratios exceeding the equivalent of the rock load could be attained, while, as a result of further deposition, ratios below the equivalent of hydrostatic could arise. An example of the latter kind could occur when an oil accumulation is well sealed in beds below an unconformity and the pressure now observed could be considered in part to be inherited. The pressures observed would not be the same as at the time of sealing, because of changes in temperature associated with changes in cover.

Broadly, it would seem that oil accumulations in lenticular reservoir rocks would be more likely to show pressures exceeding hydrostatic values than those in more extensive reservoir rocks.

In discussing the reservoir pressures of the Anaco area Funkhouser, Sass, and Hedberg[1] note that nearly all the abnormal pressures (high values for the pressure: depth ratio) are in the Oficina formation, which has widely spaced, sandy, permeable bodies constituting about 8 per cent. of an otherwise shaly section. The underlying Merecure formation has thick and extensive sandstones, and observations of reservoir pressures in it are, with few exceptions, fairly close to hydrostatic. These data are in general agreement with the expectation that pressure: depth ratios are more likely to be near hydrostatic in extensive sand bodies than in more lenticular sandstones. Diminution of pressures with depth, or a pressure difference less than would be equivalent to a water column between two sand bodies indicates a tendency for water to flow downwards through the separating shales from the shallow to the deeper reservoir, unless the intervening beds are absolutely impermeable.

Observations in the Greater Oficina area show a pressure gradient in the Oficina formation from $-3,050$ ft. to $-6,950$ ft., which is equal to that of a column of water, but extrapolation suggests that the surface water-table should be at 200 ft. above sea-level. Actually the water-table in the Mesa and Sacacual sands is 700–1,000 ft. above sea-level, showing that the Freites shale over the Oficina formation must constitute a barrier to the attainment of hydrostatic equilibrium between the surface beds and the Oficina oil reservoirs.

Derived pressure

Suppose there are two permeable rocks at considerably different depths, and initially not in fluid connexion by an avenue of appreciable permeability. Let their volumes and pressures be, respectively, V_s and V_d, and P_s and P_d, where the suffixes s and d denote shallow and deep. The difference in depth is h. A fracture is formed which provides a permeable connexion between these two permeable rocks. The opening of the fracture will lead to a pressure drop which will be dependent on the volume of the fracture relative to the volumes of V_s and V_d. However, apart from this the opening of the connexion could, under certain circumstances, lead to a rise in the pressure in the shallower reservoir. Such circumstances would exist when, after allowing for the pressure drop in the lower reservoir due to filling the fracture, the pressure in that reservoir still exceeded V_s by more than $h\rho$, where ρ is the density of the fluid in the fracture. In this case there would be flow from the deep to the shallow reservoir causing a drop in the pressure in the former and a rise in the latter. When flow ceased the two pressures would differ by $h\rho$, and the pressure changes in the two reservoirs would be dependent on the relative values of V_s, V_d, and v, the last being the volume of the fracture. If v is negligible, and V_s small compared with V_d, the pressure rise in the shallow reservoir would be relatively large; but if V_d is small compared with V_s the pressure change in the shallow reservoir would be comparatively small. Again, a mechanism is indicated whereby the pressure: depth ratio for a reservoir could seem abnormal. The 'abnormal' pressure in the shallow reservoir could be considered to be a 'derived' pressure.

When the initial pressure difference between the two reservoirs is less than $h\rho$, there will be flow from the upper reservoir to the lower reservoir if equilibrium has not been attained when the storage capacity of the crack has been satisfied.

In order to give point to the discussion on the effect of putting two widely separated reservoirs into communication the following case has been examined numerically:

The deep reservoir at 4,000 p.s.i. and 60° C. contains 100 million barrels of oil and 200 million barrels of water.

The shallow reservoir at 2,000 p.s.i. and 40° C. contains 50 million barrels of oil and 200 million barrels of water.

The reservoirs are 2,000 ft. apart vertically; the oil has the properties of that in Fig. 4, while the water conforms with the data of Fig. 5.

If the connecting crack is of negligible volume and connects the two water zones, the pressure in the shallow reservoir will increase by 705 p.s.i., while the pressure in the deep reservoir will fall by 430 p.s.i. If the crack is 1 mile long, 2,000 ft. high, and 0·4 in. wide, the corresponding figures will be approximately 687 p.s.i. and 448 p.s.i. In both cases the shallower reservoir after connexion will have a seemingly anomalous pressure—a pressure which is above rock load if the reservoir is 2,000 ft. deep; the pressure:depth ratios would be 1·352 p.s.i./ft. and 1·343 p.s.i./ft., respectively, for these two cases.

A number of factors in addition to hydrostatic head, compaction, and lateral pressure can contribute in some measure to determining the value of the reservoir pressure.

Change in depth of burial

It is of some interest to try to determine the effect on the space occupied by an oil or gas accumulation when its depth of burial is changed. Such a change will lead to changes in the pressure and temperature under which the oil and gas are stored.

Some features of the behaviour of the accumulation on change in depth of burial can readily be predicted from a study of the phase diagrams shown in Fig. 1. An oil accumulation with a gas cap will be represented by a point such as A. When the depth of burial is increased the pressure and temperature will both rise and the system will follow some path on the diagram such as $A-B$. For small increases in burial there may be diminution in the size of the gas cap; but if the change causes the system to cross the bubble-point line the gas cap will disappear, and there will be an under-saturated oil accumulation.

In quantitative studies two general conditions must be considered: (a) the pressure is hydrostatic and directly related to the thickness of cover (assuming that reservoir rock outcrop levels and field surface levels are substantially the same); and (b) the reservoir is sealed, and hence the pressure is determined in some measure by rock load or rock strength.

(a) If there is freely mobile edge-water and hydrostatic pressure, then the movement in edge-water on changing the depth of burial of the gas or oil accumulation will be determined by the difference in volume change of the hydrocarbons (dV) and the change in volume of the reservoir storage space (dv), i.e. it is $dV-dv$.

The change in volume of the hydrocarbons can be estimated from a knowledge of the change in depth of burial, the temperature and pressure gradients, together with the pressure-volume relationships of the hydrocarbon systems at different temperatures. Fig. 4 provides a basis for the discussion. The data presented relate to a system of Dominguez crude with 5·61 per cent. (by weight) of gas. Superimposed on the isotherms are curves which allow the temperatures to rise by 1° C./100 ft. or 1° C./200 ft. of burial. The surface temperature is taken as 15° C., and the pressure gradient is hydrostatic (0·43 p.s.i./ft.). These curves indicate that the system has a minimum volume at the bubble-point; at lower pressures there is a relatively rapid increase in specific volume (this will be associated with a gas cap of increasing mass); at higher pressures (greater depths of burial) there will be a small increase in volume. The increase will be of the order of 0·00064 per cent. per ft. of increased cover with a temperature gradient of 1° C./100 ft., and 0·00017 per cent. per ft. for a temperature gradient of 1° C./200 ft.

The coefficient of thermal expansion of sandstone at atmospheric pressure is approximately $30\pm6\times10^{-6}$ for temperatures of 20°–100° C. Under increasing pressure this figure will be reduced a little. Thus an increase of 2,000 ft. in depth of burial of a sandstone will cause an increase in volume of about 0·06 per cent. when the temperature gradient is 1° C./200 ft. It is assumed that the forces to which the rock is subjected do not exceed its crushing strength, and therefore the pore volume will increase proportionately to the increase in bulk volume.

The same increase in depth of burial of a hydrocarbon system such as that shown in Fig. 4 and initially at a pressure exceeding the bubble-point will give a volume increase of 1·28 per cent. for a temperature gradient of 1° C./200 ft. and of 0·34 per cent. for a temperature gradient of 1° C./200 ft. Ignoring the expansion of any interstitial water the additional bulk volume of reservoir rock occupied by the oil on deeper burial will be 1·28 per cent. −0·06 per cent. = 1·22 per cent. in the former case, and 0·34 per cent. −0·03 per cent. = 0·31 per cent. in the latter case.

(b) When the accumulation is sealed, so that there is no possibility of really free edge-water movement, the problem is more complex. The behaviour will be dependent on the size of the reservoir (in terms of storage space), on the relative volumes occupied by the water and hydrocarbons, and on their properties. Suppose that the initial conditions of the accumulation are given by P_i, T_i, and that Fig. 4 gives the behaviour of the hydrocarbon system, while Fig. 5 gives that of the water. On increasing the depth of burial let unit volume of storage space be increased by x per cent., the new reservoir temperature being T_n. The problem of finding the new reservoir pressure P_n and the change in the oil-water level can be solved as follows: Suppose that the initial volumes of hydrocarbons and water are V_h' and V_w', respectively. Then points must be selected on the T_n isotherms of Figs. 4 and 5 which are at the same pressure P_n and for which the respective volumes of hydrocarbons and water, namely, V_h'' and V_w'', satisfy the following conditions:

$$\frac{(V_h'' + V_w'')100}{V_h' + V_w'} = 100 + x \text{ per cent.}$$

Any change in position of the hydrocarbon-water contact as a result of the change in depth of burial will be revealed by comparison of the ratios V_h''/V_w'' and V_h'/V_w'.

Suppose that the sealed accumulation is at a temperature of 40° C. and under a pressure of 1,750 p.s.i.a.; that the ratio of water to oil (with dissolved gas) in the accumulation is 4:1; that there is no gas cap; that the sandstone reservoir is buried an additional 2,000 ft. and thereby the temperature rises by 20° C. Trial-and-error procedure shows that a pressure slightly exceeding 4,250 p.s.i.a. will satisfy the conditions of allowing the volume of oil plus water to be 0·06 per cent. greater than originally. Thus the perfectly sealed condition visualized leads to a pressure rise of over 2,500 p.s.i., which is somewhat greater than the added rock load, allowing 1 p.s.i./ft. of added cover. In the course of the deeper burial the volume of the oil will decrease slightly, while the water will occupy a somewhat greater volume than under the original conditions. The retention of the accumulation under the new conditions will require some measure of mechanical strength in the cover rocks. For a 1:1 ratio of oil and water in the sealed accumulation and other conditions as before the pressure increase would be 2,350 p.s.i. (approximately).

Had the initial pressure been 1,500 p.s.i., with a temperature of 40° C., and the volumetric ratio of water to hydrocarbons of 4:1, burial by an additional 2,000 ft. of sediments would have resulted in a reservoir pressure slightly over 2,500 p.s.i. (the temperature is assumed to have risen by 20° C., while the properties of the oil and water are the same as before). Under the initial conditions there would be a gas cap, but this would disappear in the course of burial, and under the final reservoir conditions the oil would be undersaturated with gas. The pressure rise of only 1,000 p.s.i. in the course of deeper burial, instead of more than 2,500 p.s.i. indicated in the first example, is a consequence of the greater compressibility of the hydrocarbon system under the lower pressures considered.

In the above numerical examples the specific volume-pressure-temperature data of Fig. 5 have been used. These data are for pure water.[2] Specific volume-pressure data for sea-water[6] at 0° C. have a similar slope, i.e. the compressibility is approximately the same as for pure water. It is, however, probable that the water associated with an oil and gas accumulation would have some dissolved gas as well as dissolved salts, and the presence of dissolved gas might increase the compressibility of the water. The extent of the increase would be dependent on a number of factors. The method of solving the problem set out above would be unchanged for water with dissolved salts and gas in the sealed reservoir along with the oil, but quantitative studies would require the use of the appropriate specific volume-pressure-temperature data. The effect of a greater compressibility for the water would be a smaller rise in pressure than for pure water.

Water with 9·4 cu. ft./brl. of dissolved gas had a compressibility of $3·47 \times 10^{-6}$ vol./vol./p.s.i. The measured compressibility of the East Texas brine is reported to be $2·66 \times 10^{-6}$ vol./vol./p.s.i. The effective compressibility of the East Texas aquifer derived by Rumble, Spain, and Stamm[5] was $7·63 \times 10^{-6}$ vol./vol./p.s.i. These figures compare with about $2·63 \times 10^{-6}$ vol./vol./p.s.i. for pure water at 40° C. in the range 0–2,000 p.s.i. Apparently high values for water compressibility in oil-producing formations are sometimes assumed to be due to pockets of free gas in the aquifer or to compaction effects.

It may be noted that if the sealed accumulation consisted only of gas-oil solution with the properties shown in Fig. 4 or of this solution with water which, because of dissolved gas or other substances, had the same compressibility and thermal expansion as the oil, the pressure increase due to the deeper burial postulated would be 2,280 p.s.i. The water would then have a compressibility about four times the value for pure water in Fig. 5, while its coefficient of thermal expansion under pressures ranging 2,000–4,000 p.s.i. would be nearly three times that for pure water.

Chemical and physico-chemical changes

Chemical break-down or polymerization of the hydrocarbons in a *sealed* reservoir would, respectively, cause an increase or a decrease in pressure. The evolution of more hydrocarbons from source material would possibly cause a pressure rise. However, the occurrence of break-down or further evolution of hydrocarbons in a mature oil accumulation is a debatable matter. Certain chemical changes, broadly referred to as weathering, are believed to take place in hydrocarbon accumulations which are near the surface. It is improbable that these will lead to marked pressure changes since the conditions requisite for the reactions to take place involve relatively free fluid connexion with the ground surface. Such a connexion will control the pressure in the oil zone.

Recrystallization of a reservoir rock, whether caused by lateral or vertical pressure, leads to a reduction in porosity, and is therefore the same as compaction in its effect on fluids in the reservoir rock.

The deposition of cement inside an already sealed reservoir could lead to pressure changes if, as is probable, the volume of cement-bearing solution differs from the volume of the deposited cement plus the former solvent. Pressure changes on this account seem likely to be small.

A brine from the Embar at Little Buffalo Basin, Wyoming, had 756 p.p.m. of calcium and 1,525 p.p.m. of bicarbonate ion. Using these data as a basis for discussion it is evident that such a brine would be capable of giving 1,890 p.p.m. of calcium carbonate if the whole of the calcium were deposited in this form. Assuming that the volume of a solution containing this quantity of potential calcium carbonate is the same as the volume of solvent, and that the solvent density is 1·0, the volume of 998·11 c.c. will yield 1·89 gm. of calcite. The latter will occupy 0·695 c.c. There are various approximations in the preceding statement, but it appears that deposition of *all* the calcite could lead to an expansion of only 0·07 per cent. The mean compressibility of sea-water diminishes as the temperature rises from 0° C. to 30° C., and at the lower temperatures it diminishes as the range of pressure is increased. For the range up to 1,000 bars (atmospheres) a mean value of 4×10^{-5} vol./vol./bar may be reasonable. Hence a change of 0·07 per cent. (or 0·0007 per unit volume) would be equivalent to a pressure increase of the order of 17·5 bars (about 260 p.s.i.). However, it is probable that even if all the calcite were deposited from the above solution the expansion would be less than indicated. The full deposition would probably not occur, and hence the associated pressure rise in a sealed, water-charged reservoir might be much less than 250 p.s.i. Should the reservoir rock contain hydrocarbons as well as water, the rise in pressure due to deposition of calcium carbonate would be even smaller.

In a sandstone of uniform spherical, close-packed grains, the porosity would be about 26 per cent. Unit volume of sandstone would have 0·00018 c.c. of calcite deposited from the contained water under the circumstances assumed in the preceding paragraph. It is doubtful whether such a small amount of calcite, if spread evenly over grain surfaces, would be visible. It is apparent, therefore, that microscopically recognizable amounts of calcite would be obtainable only by many pore volumes of such a water passing through the rock, and not from the static water content.

Lastly, mineralogical changes in the clays or shales adjacent to reservoir rocks have been suggested as a cause of reservoir pressure changes, usually in a downward direction. It is postulated that the clay minerals take up water from the rock pores with a probable over-all reduction in volume of water plus original mineral grains. The magnitude and even the feasibility of volume changes of this type are highly speculative matters in the present state of knowledge. It may, however, be hazarded that the changes are small, if they occur at all.

REFERENCES

1. FUNKHOUSER, H. J., SASS, L. C., and HEDBERG, H. D., *Bull. Amer. Assoc. Petrol. Geol.*, **32**, 1851–1908 (1948).
2. GORANSON, R. W., *Handbook of Physical Constants*, Geol. Soc. of America, Special Paper No. 56.
3. KEEP, C. E., and WARD, H. L., *J. Inst. Pet. Tech.*, **29**, 990–1013 (1934).
4. MUSKAT, M., *Physical Principles of Oil Production*, McGraw-Hill Book Co. Inc., 1949.
5. RUMBLE, R. C., SPAIN, H. J., and STAMM, H. E., *J. Petrol. Tech.*, **3**, 331–40, A.I.M.M.E. Tech. Paper No. 3219 (1951).
6. SVERDRUP, H. V., JOHNSON, M. W., and FLEMING, R. H., *The Oceans*, 1053, Prentice-Hall, Inc., 1942.
7. VAN HORN, F. R., *Trans. A.I.M.M.E.*, **56**, 831–42 (1916).

APPENDIX I

COMPACTION

SOME sediments are laid down with a porosity which remains substantially unaltered even when they become deeply buried. Other sediments are deposited with a large porosity, but as they are buried the porosity diminishes and may ultimately become as small as, or even smaller than, that of the first type of sediment. The sediments which undergo a marked diminution in porosity on burial are said to be compactible, and the process of diminution in porosity is known as compaction. Broadly, the finer the grain size of the sediment the greater the compactibility. Thus, sands undergo no marked compaction, except in cases of very deep burial wherein, due to solution and re-deposition, the porosity is reduced simultaneously with a change in shape of the grains. On the other hand, shales and clays start as muds which undergo extensive compaction. It is likely that ultimately there may be some measure of mineralogical change in these deposits, a further feature in which they differ from the sands. Fine-grained sediments commonly differ in mineral composition from the coarser sediments. Limestones are formed in a number of different ways, and these involve original sediments of markedly different grain sizes. The coarser calcareous deposits—the shell breccias, and calcareous sands— behave mainly like ordinary silica sands except that solution and re-deposition may occur before burial is deep, while the finer deposits—the calcareous muds—undergo compaction like clays and shales.

The sediments in most oilfield areas include considerable thicknesses of clays or shales. Indeed, it has been stated that such deposits may average about 70 per cent. of the sediments penetrated in oilfield development. Moreover, it has been indicated that many oil source rocks are probably clays or shales. Fine-grained rocks also act as cap-rocks. Hence oilfield areas have considerable thicknesses of compactible beds.

Athy[1] and Hedberg[2] have been prominent amongst the geologists who have investigated the relationship between porosity and depth of burial of clays and shales, and who have discussed the geological consequences of compaction. Although these two workers put forward appreciably different depth-porosity relationships, their general conclusions agreed in showing a rapid drop in porosity for small depths of burial and a progressive diminution in the rate of porosity reduction as the depth of burial increased. In view of the difficulties inherent in studies of this type and the variability of rocks, the differences in their detailed depth-porosity relationships are not surprising.

Fig. 35 shows the relationships proposed by Athy and Hedberg.

Two aspects of the phenomenon of compaction are of special interest in petroleum geology. These are the amount and rate of loss of fluids from compacting sediments, and the development of structures when deposition and compaction take place over an uneven surface.

Fluid loss. From a depth-porosity curve a further curve relating depth and fluid content in a prism of sediments can be derived.[3] A complementary curve relates the depth and the amount of solid matter (reduced depth) in the same prism. The area under the depth-porosity curve between any two depths is proportional to the total pore space, i.e. to the fluid content, between those two depths. The difference between the true depth and the reduced depth is

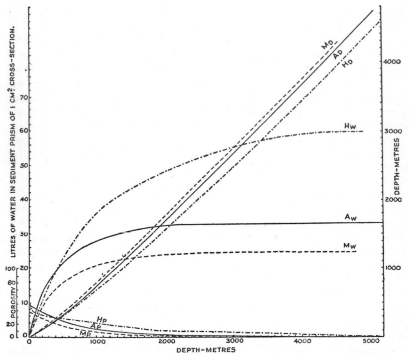

FIG. 35. *AP*, *HP* and *MP* are curves of porosity plotted against true depth. A_D, H_D, and M_D are curves of reduced depth plotted against true depth. A_W, H_W, and M_W are curves of the volume of water in a 1-cm.² prism plotted against the reduced depth. *A* indicates that the sediment obeys Athy's compaction law, *H* that it obeys Hedberg's law, and *M* that the sediment has 30 per cent. of non-compactible beds, the compactible beds obeying Athy's law.

a measure of the aggregate pore space (fluid content) over any depth interval. Fig. 35 shows the true depth-reduced depth relationship based on Athy's equation and on Hedberg's data, and also gives the water content of a rock column of 1-cm.² cross-section versus reduced depth for the same two sets of basic data.

If it is reasonable to assume that shale samples representative of different depths in the column were identical or at least similar when deposited, then each point in the column may be considered to represent a stage in the history of any sample which now lies at a greater depth. A further assumption implicit in this suggestion is that the basic data are for compactible beds in equilibrium with the load, i.e. that the beds have reached their maximum degree of compaction for the load shown.

A given section of sediment (i.e. a section between two given markers) will have a constant reduced thickness whatever its depth of burial, whereas the real thickness will diminish as burial increases. For uniform material the

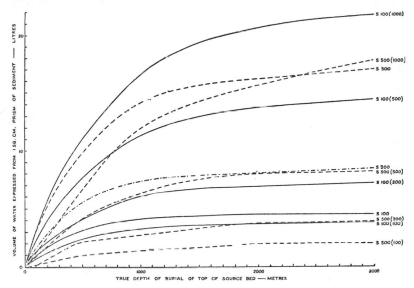

FIG. 36. Curves S 100, S 200, and S 500 give the volume of liquid squeezed from source rock sections which were, respectively, 100 m., 200 m., and 500 m. thick as deposited, when they are buried to the depths shown. Curves with a number in brackets refer to the water squeezed from the rock section below the source rock and above a major unconformity, the number giving the thickness of this rock section when the deposition of the source rock was just complete. The source rock and the beds are assumed to obey Athy's law. The number before the brackets shows the initial thickness of the source rock overlying the compacting beds.

reduced-thickness device permits the recognition of a given section of sediment and its behaviour as it is progressively buried more and more deeply.

Since, on the basis of the assumptions indicated, the behaviour of a certain section of compacting beds can be followed as it is more and more deeply buried, the amount of water expressed by compaction can be determined. Fig. 36 (curves S 100, S 200, and S 500) shows the volume of water expressed at various depths of burial for a series of compactible beds of different thicknesses, without the transmission of any water from an underlying compactible group. Fig. 37 is a comparable diagram with, however, the depth of burial expressed as a reduced depth instead of the true depth employed in Fig. 36. Very considerable volumes of water must be squeezed from each unit prism of the compactible sediment, quite apart from any water which enters from underlying beds (Fig. 36, curves S 100 (100), S 100 (200), S 100 (500), S 100 (1,000), &c.). This water will travel mainly upwards, although there can be some downward travel in certain cases. The flow will probably be fairly evenly distributed. Extensive lateral flow such as would be required to feed a relatively limited number of vertical channels seems unlikely.

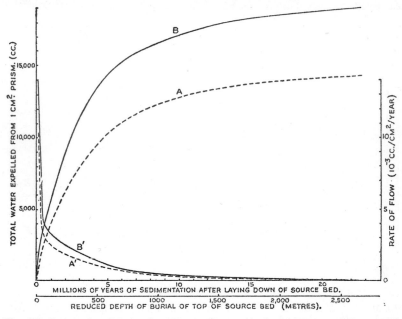

FIG. 37. Curves A and B are for 100 m. of source bed over 500 m. of compactible beds above a major unconformity; A gives the water expelled from the beds below the source rock, and B the water expelled from both series of beds. Curves A' and B' show, respectively, the bulk rate of fluid flow per 1 cm.^{2} into the bottom or out of the top of the source bed for an assumed rate of deposition of 0·02 gm. (weight in water)/cm.^{2}/year.

If the rate of sedimentation of the beds overlying a group which is undergoing compaction is uniform, the average rates of flow of water into the base and out of the top of the group will be proportional to the slopes of curves A and B (Fig. 37) at any reduced depth of burial. Curves A' and B' (Fig. 37) were obtained by the application of this principle, and show the average rates of flow into the base and out of the top of a ' 100 m.' section (true thickness when deposition just completed) of source rock resting on a further ' 500 m.' of compactible beds, for an assumed uniform rate of deposition of the overlying beds.

The rates of flow decrease relatively rapidly as the depth of burial increases. The general form of the relationship and the relative values of the rates are far more important than the actual numerical values shown on Fig. 37.

If compaction fluids provide the motive power for primary oil migration it would appear that conditions would be most favourable for the occurrence of that process during the period before the oil source rock becomes deeply buried. Both the volume of fluid available and its bulk rate of flow decrease as time passes, while the rock pores diminish in size, making the passage of fluids more difficult in some senses, but nevertheless some flow is inevitable until compaction ceases.

The paths followed by compaction fluids in a series of beds consisting of coarse- and fine-grained deposits depend on many factors, but they will be determined by the principle of the minimum utilization of energy. The significant factors will be the permeabilities of the two types of beds, the individual thicknesses and distribution of these beds, and their geometry. The thickness of the compacting beds, and nearness to compacted but permeable basement, are also important. Where the geometry is favourable advantage will be taken of lengthened paths in the more permeable beds, but it seems probable that only when the latter outcrop relatively near by will there be movement substantially parallel to the bedding. On other occasions there will be some deflexion of the paths from verticality, and obliquity of flow near areas of minimum cover of the low permeability beds. The greater the relative variation in the cover the greater will be this deflexion.

The detailed paths of the fluid expelled during compaction may change appreciably with time and with depth of burial, because the thickness and the permeability of the compactible beds will diminish. Secondly, even sands may have some diminution in permeability due to deposition of cements from fluids in transit. This deposition may be more prominent in some parts of the sands than in others, with the non-uniformity causing a shift of the flow lines. The possibility of some solution, with an increase in permeability, cannot be excluded in certain types of rock, while dolomitization and recrystallization are other processes which may cause permeability changes with the passage of time, in rocks which can commonly function as oil reservoir rocks and in which oblique flow is most likely. Furthermore, the geometry of the beds may change with time, and faulting may create new avenues for flow, these being additional features which may change the paths of flow.

Closure developed by compaction over buried hills. The reduced depth-true depth curves can be used to determine the amount of closure to be expected in structures formed over buried hills by compaction. Again, assumptions have to be made about the constitution of the compacting series in terms of compactible and non-compactible series, and the properties of the former. However, the direction of flow of the compaction fluids is no longer important, except that locally and temporarily it may affect the rate of compaction. All that matters ultimately as regards the form of the beds is that the fluids are driven out of the sediments.

Suppose that there is a hill on a buried landscape and that this rises 200 m. above the general level of the surrounding area (Fig. 38). Let its crest be covered by sediment to a depth of 300 m. while the surrounding area has a maximum of 500 m., so that the top of the sediment is horizontal at this stage. If a marker bed is laid down at this stage, after which deposition continues until there is 800 m. of beds over the crest of the hill and a maximum of 1,000 m. in the surrounding area, the form of the marker bed which will arise as a result of compaction can be obtained.

Assuming that the compacting series obeys Athy's law the reduced depth corresponding with 1,000 m. true depth is 744 m.; that corresponding with 500 m. true depth is 327 m. The difference in reduced depth of 417 m. corresponds with the amount of sediment laid on top of the marker bed in the area around the hill, and is equivalent to 610 m. true depth, i.e. the depth of the marker bed after compaction is 610 m. Over the top of the hill 800 m.

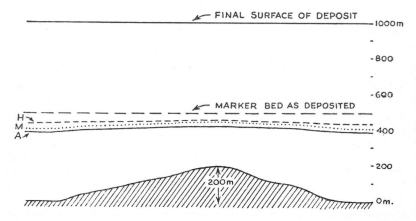

FIG. 38. Structural closure due to compaction of beds over a buried hill. *A*, final position of marker bed if sediments obey Athy's law; *H*, final position of marker bed if sediments obey Hedberg's law; *M*, final position of marker bed if sediments have 30 per cent. of non-compactible beds, and the compactible beds obey Athy's law.

true depth corresponds with 570 m. reduced depth, and 300 m. true depth corresponds with 181 m. reduced depth. The difference in reduced depth of 389 m., which is equivalent to 575 m. true depth, is the amount of cover over the marker bed at this point. Hence the closure developed in the marker bed by the compaction of the enclosing series is 610–575 = 35 m. Had the compacting beds obeyed Hedberg's relationship, with the other conditions unaltered, the closure developed would be 22 m.; if the compactible group obeyed Athy's law, but included 30 per cent. of non-compactible beds, the closure would be 32 m. The marked difference in computed closure resulting from the use of the different relationships should be noted. Clearly, local knowledge is needed to obtain a figure which is more than a general indication of the possible closure.

If, as is most likely, the sediment does not attain the horizontal upper surface postulated above, the marker bed and other beds will have initial dips which will be changed by further deposition and compaction. The final closure can, nevertheless, still be derived in the above manner.

The same method can be employed to predict the closure which would be developed when there is uplift during sedimentation and therefore a factor in addition to compaction and depositional dips contributing to the total closure.

REFERENCES

1. ATHY, L. F., *Bull. Amer. Assoc. Petrol. Geol.*, **14,** 1 (1930).
2. HEDBERG, H. D., *Amer. J. Science*, 5th series, **31,** 241 (1936).
3. HOBSON, G. D., *J. Inst. Pet.*, **29,** 37–54 (1943).
4. JONES, O. T., *Quart. J. Geol. Soc. (London)*, **100,** 137 56 (1944).
5. SKEMPTON, A. W., ibid., 119–35 (1944).

APPENDIX II

DEFINITIONS

Formation volume factor. Suppose that a volume V of the reservoir oil (oil with gas in solution, and at the reservoir temperature and pressure) is brought to the surface. Under the surface pressure and temperature gas will be evolved and the oil, substantially free of gas, will occupy a volume v. The formation volume factor is the ratio V/v. It is greater than unity, and the change in volume in changing from subsurface to surface conditions is referred to as shrinkage. Formation volume factors exceeding 3·3 have been noted.

Porosity. The porosity of a rock sample is the ratio of the total pore space to the bulk volume of the sample. It is commonly expressed as a percentage. There are rock specimens in which not all of the pores are interconnected. Such isolated pores are of no value from the point of view of commercial oil production. As a consequence, in petroleum production only the interconnected pore space which can be put in communication with a well is of interest. Such pore space provides the *effective porosity* of the rock, and must be distinguished from the total or *net porosity*.

Permeability. The permeability of a rock is a measure of the ease with which fluids can pass through it. The formal definition is $K = \dfrac{VL}{PA}\,\eta$, where V is rate of flow in c.c./sec., η the viscosity of the fluid in centipoises, P the pressure drop in atmospheres over a length of L cm. in the direction of flow, and A is the area in sq. cm. through which the flow is taking place. K is the permeability in darcys. The value obtained with a single fluid which does not interact with the rock is the *specific permeability*. Permeabilities are commonly expressed in thousandths of a darcy, i.e. in millidarcys (mD).

When the rock contains minerals of the clay group the permeability may be a function of the salinity or acidity of the water which is flowing. This is due to certain interactions between the fluid or ions in it and the clay particles. The differences in permeability due to this phenomenon can be large; differences of smaller magnitude have been observed between measurements with air and water, and a comparable explanation is given for part of these differences.

In oil reservoir rocks there are invariably two and sometimes three fluids in the producing zones. As a consequence the conditions are more complex than those visualized in the simple definition of specific permeability given earlier. When more than one fluid is present in a piece of rock under test the rate of flow of each fluid can be measured and associated with the appropriate viscosity, pressure gradient, and rock dimensions in order to calculate the *effective permeability* of the rock to that fluid in the presence of the other fluid or fluids. It has been found convenient to make use of the *relative permeability* which is the ratio of the effective and specific permeabilities of the specimens for a given fluid. The relative and effective permeabilities are dependent on the proportion of the total pore space occupied by the fluid in question, and it is possible that they are dependent in some measure also on the actual fluid distribution.

Fig. 39 shows the typical form of the relationship between relative permeability and the proportions of the fluids in the pores. As the saturation of a fluid decreases, so there is a decrease in the relative permeability for that fluid. Furthermore, the permeability to a given fluid becomes zero before the saturation of that fluid is zero. This phenomenon accounts for the production of

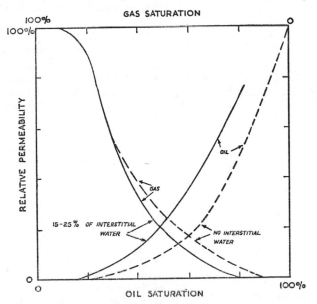

FIG. 39. Relative permeability-saturation curves (after Leverett).

water-free oil from a zone of rock in which there may be 20 per cent. or more of interstitial water. The water saturation below which the permeability of the rock to water is zero is known as the irreducible minimum in *capillary pressure* studies. The interrelations of porosity and permeability are complex, the only universally applicable statement being that a rock must be porous in order to be permeable.

In non-isotropic rocks the permeability is dependent on the direction of flow. For rocks *in situ* the permeability will be determined not only by the pore size, structure, and frequency, but also by such features as joints and fissures.

Capillary pressure. If a specimen of sandstone is saturated with water and placed on a water-wet tissue pad on top of a sintered glass disk (which will have very fine pores) the water in the sandstone will be continuous with that in the tissue and in the sintered glass disk. Suppose that the disk is so mounted (Fig. 40) and that air pressure can be applied to the outside of the sandstone.

If the air pressure is slowly raised a point will be reached at which air will begin to enter the pores of the sandstone, and in this process water will be displaced and pass through to be collected below the sintered glass disk. If the air pressure is kept constant at the value at which penetration of the sandstone begins it will be found that after a time the expulsion of water will cease. A further increase in pressure may cause the expulsion of more water, and the measurements involve raising the pressure in steps, allowing time for equilibrium (for the maximum expulsion of water) to be reached at each pressure. This process is continued until a pressure is reached above which no further expulsion of water occurs. The water then remaining in the sandstone is known as the *irreducible minimum saturation*, provided that the pores of the sintered glass disk are smaller than any of the pores in the sandstone. The amount of water expelled for each pressure increment can be determined by observation of the volume collected, or by finding the loss in weight of the sandstone.

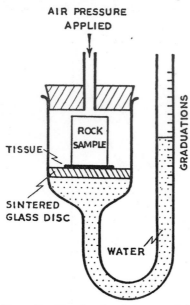

FIG. 40. Sketch showing essential features of apparatus for the measurement of capillary pressures.

A knowledge of the total pore space in the sandstone specimen permits the various amounts of water expelled to be expressed as a percentage of the total pore space. A graph connecting the applied pressure and the water saturation of the core is known as a *capillary pressure curve*. The shape of the curve is dependent on the surface tension of the water, and on the interrelationships and distribution of pore sizes and forms, and throat sizes in the sandstone. A comparable curve could be obtained by displacing the water by oil. The form would be the same as for air and water, but the ratio of the pressures at corresponding water saturations would be the ratio of the surface tension of water and the interfacial tension between oil and water.

The pressure at which air begins to enter the water-saturated sandstone is the *displacement pressure*. It is determined by the size of the largest pores on the exposed surface of the sandstone, and the surface tension of the water. If r is the radius of curvature of the air lobe entering such pores the excess pressure over atmospheric will be $p = 2T/r$, T being the surface tension of the water. Comparable relationships will hold for the curvature of the air-water interfaces at each stage. At the irreducible minimum the water occurs as a wetting film on the sand grains, as collars round grain contacts, and as fillings of some pores. The last two forms account for the bulk of the water. Completely water-filled pores are left when the invading air isolates them and leaves no water connexion with the sintered glass disk except via wetting films, which apparently do not transmit water.

The capillary properties, as indicated in capillary pressure measurements, in conjunction with the appropriate interfacial tensions and fluid densities fix the fluid distributions in the oil-water and gas-oil transition zones in an oil reservoir. They, together with the height in the accumulation and the fluid density differences, determine the interstitial water content of the reservoir rock; the irreducible minimum is reached only when the oil column exceeds

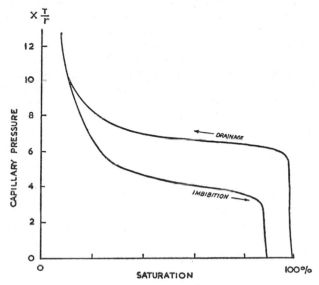

Fig. 41. Capillary pressure curves (after Haines). The units of the pressure scale are the quotient of the surface tension and effective pore radius.

a critical height. It should be noted that the local capillary structure of the reservoir is of paramount importance.

Capillary pressure curves obtained by displacement of the wetting fluid from the porous medium (drainage) are not necessarily the same as those determined when the wetting fluid saturation is gradually increased (imbibition) (Fig. 41).

The phenomena involved in capillary pressure studies are comparable with those which operate in the process of forming an oil accumulation. This process involves the displacement of water by oil in the porous rock, i.e. it is equivalent to the drainage approach. In Nature the necessary pressure differences in reservoir rocks are provided by the differences in density between the fluids. When an oil accumulation undergoes readjustments due to disturbance of the equilibrium both drainage and imbibition phenomena may be involved.

The capillary pressure at a given oil saturation increases as the pore size of the rock decreases. Hence at a given horizontal plane intersecting adjacent rocks of different pore sizes containing oil and water, each continuously connected, the oil saturation will be least in the rock with the finest pores.

Spilling plane. The spilling plane is the highest level at which hydrocarbons can escape from a sealed trap by reason of their having filled the trap to its maximum capacity. In the case of an anticlinal trap it will be the level of the top of the reservoir rock in the highest adjacent syncline or saddle. Thus in Fig. 31 the top of the reservoir rock in the syncline between domes Q and R will mark a spilling plane, provided that the section passes through the highest part of that syncline. The spilling plane corresponds in level with the lowest closed contour which can be drawn round a simple dome, e.g. in Fig. 32 a spilling plane would exist at a level of about $-1,460$ ft., in the saddle between the minor dome on the right and the higher twin domes on the left.

The above is the conventional usage of the term 'spilling plane', and it implies the level of a surface under which the hydrocarbons flow to escape from the trap they have filled. However, in some cases the maximum size of the hydrocarbon accumulation is fixed by the level of the lowest point at which water can spill over to escape from a trap as hydrocarbons enter the trap. (See discussion of fluid adjustments associated with faulting on p. 94. There are, however, other circumstances where a spill-over level for water will fix the final position of the hydrocarbon-water contact.)

Closure. The *height of closure* is the difference in level between the spilling plane and the highest point of the top of the reservoir rock in the trap. The *area of closure*, in the case of a simple dome, is the area enclosed by the contour drawn at the level of the spilling plane. It represents the maximum area of hydrocarbon accumulation possible in the structure when the gas-water or the oil-water contact is horizontal.

REFERENCES

Porosity

COOMBER, S. E., *Science of Petroleum*, i, 220–3, Oxford University Press, 1938.
MUSKAT, M., *Physical Principles of Oil Production*, McGraw-Hill Book Co. Inc., 1949.

Permeability

GEFFEN, T. M., OWENS, W. W., PARRISH, D. R., and MORSE, R. A., *J. Petrol. Tech.*, 3 (4), A.I.M.M.E. Tech. Paper No. 3053 (1951).
HASSLER, G. L., *Science of Petroleum*, i, 198–208, Oxford University Press, 1938.
LEVERETT, M. C., *Petrol. Tech.*, 1, A.I.M.M.E. Tech. Pub. No. 1003 (1938).
LEVERETT, M. C., and LEWIS, W. B., ibid., 3, A.I.M.M.E. Tech. Pub. No. 1206 (1940).
MUSKAT, M., *Physical Principles of Oil Production*, McGraw-Hill Book Co. Inc., 1949.
OSOBA, J. S., RICHARDSON, J. G., KERVER, J. K., HAFFORD, J. A., and BLAIR, P. M., ibid., 3 (2), A.I.M.M.E. Tech. Paper No. 3020 (1951).

Capillary pressure

BURDINE, N. T., GOURNAY, L. S., and REICHERTZ, P. P., ibid., 2 (7), A.I.M.M.E. Tech. Paper No. 3893 (1950).

CALHOUN, J. C., LEWIS, M., and NEWMAN, R. C., ibid., **1** (7), A.I.M.M.E. Tech. Paper No. 2640 (1949).

HAINES, W. B., *J. Agric. Sci.*, **20**, 97–116 (1930).

MUSKAT, M., *Physical Principles of Oil Production*, McGraw-Hill Book Co. Inc., 1949.

APPENDIX III

ADDENDUM

SINCE the manuscript of the previous pages was sent to the printers two important articles have appeared which have a bearing on the matter of the origin of oil. One deals with the occurrence of hydrocarbons in young sediments,[2] and the other in particular with the interrelationships between the type of oil and the environment of deposition.[1]

Hydrocarbons in young sediments. In Smith's detailed account[2] of the examination of cores from the Gulf of Mexico and elsewhere (cf. p. 37), the view is expressed that the information suggests 'that petroleum is being formed in the present era, and that the crude product is Nature's composite of the hydrocarbon remains of many forms of marine life'. Smith notes that this is an amplification of F. C. Whitmore's hypothesis that 'the generation of petroleum in the earth is very largely a process of selection and concentration of hydrocarbons originally synthesized by the metabolism of marine (or even terrestrial) plants'.

The presence of hydrocarbons in algae and the higher plants has been noted earlier (pp. 26, 33, 36), and Smith lists further instances in insects, worms, fishes, and the higher animals. New observations showed 58 parts per million of paraffine–naphthene hydrocarbons in bluefish, 45 p.p.m. in oysters, and over 2,000 p.p.m. of paraffine–naphthene and aromatic hydrocarbons in a sample of phyto-plankton. Sisler and Zobell had concluded that paraffinic and naphthenic hydrocarbons were probably present in a CCl_4 extract from bacterial cell substance developed in a mineral salt medium (p. 60).

Paraffine–naphthene and aromatic hydrocarbons were detected in a series of samples besides those of the Grande Island core (p. 37). These samples were from salty, brackish, and freshwater deposits. Detailed investigation of the Pelican Island cores of the Mississippi delta gave the data summarized in Table XVI.

TABLE XVI

Chromatographic analysis of solvent extracts

	Average for ten clay samples	Average for three sand samples
% paraffine–naphthene . . .	14·1	48·2
% aromatic	6·0	17·2
% asphaltic	18·5	12·9
% on alumina	61·4	21·7

The sands were from depths of 314 ft., 680 ft., and 2,233 ft., while the clays were from the range 20–2,314 ft. The solvent extract which was used for chromatographic analysis averaged 38·3 per cent. of the total organic matter in the sands, and 2·9 per cent. in the clays. In the nine clay samples the hydrocarbons detected averaged 71 p.p.m. and ranged 31–203 p.p.m., based on the dried sediment; for the three sand samples the figures were 138, 113, and 11,700 p.p.m., in order of increasing depth. Smith states that the material in the sands was more petroleum-like than that in the clay sections, but that it is not known whether the hydrocarbon-rich material has moved from the clays into the sands, or whether the organic matter deposited with the sands differed from that deposited with the clays. However, much more information is needed before early migration can be taken to be proved for this series of cores.

The Grande Island cores had increasing proportions of paraffine–naphthene hydrocarbons in the solvent extract as the depth increased. The same *general trend* is seen for the seven Pelican Island clay samples down to 350 ft., but this trend does not hold for the deeper clay samples. A variety of explanations can be given for this state of affairs. Additional information on the Pelican Island section might eliminate some of the possibilities, while data from further wells in the same general environment would be desirable to show whether or not the trend in the upper sediments indicated by the two sets of cores is characteristic.

Smith's suggestion about the formation of petroleum raises a fine point about the field to be covered in any discussion of the origin of oil. A mechanism of formation in the sediments not being required, if the suggestion is correct, the main issue, once the sediments are laid down, might relate to the means of separation of crude oil from physical association with other organic matter. Indeed, until the hydrocarbons are capable of movement from the site of deposition, it could be argued that they would not effectively be crude oil from the point of view of oil accumulations. Nevertheless, if the indications of change with depth of burial represent evolution of the oil in the sediments, it would still be necessary to search for the agent or agents responsible for this change.* Moreover, the stage at which methane and possibly other light paraffins, as well as any carbon dioxide and hydrogen sulphide appear, has also to be indicated, in addition to the mechanism by which they are formed (cf. p. 39).

Environment and nature of crude. J. M. Hunt[1] has described the results of a study of the crude oils of Wyoming, and concludes that the major differences between the Wyoming crudes are due to differences in their source material and environment of deposition (cf. pp. 31, 50). The more naphthenic and aromatic oils were associated with the more saline environments of deposition, characterized by carbonates and sulphates rather than clastic sediments. For oils formed in clastic sediments the more aromatic and naphthenic types were associated with the higher sand/shale ratios, i.e. near-shore basin position. Hunt states that in the Tensleep there was some relationship with depth of burial, but that the depth factor is in general of secondary importance. If any

---

* If Brooks's views are correct the agents are presumably not heat and pressure.

chemical changes are taking place in the oil with time they are believed to be so slight as to be masked by differences due to other factors.

REFERENCES

1. HUNT, J. M., *Bull. Amer. Assoc. Petrol. Geol.*, **37** (8), 1837–72 (1953).
2. SMITH, P. V., ibid., **38** (3), 377–404 (1954).

INDEX

PRINTED IN
GREAT BRITAIN
AT THE
UNIVERSITY PRESS
OXFORD
BY
CHARLES BATEY
PRINTER
TO THE
UNIVERSITY